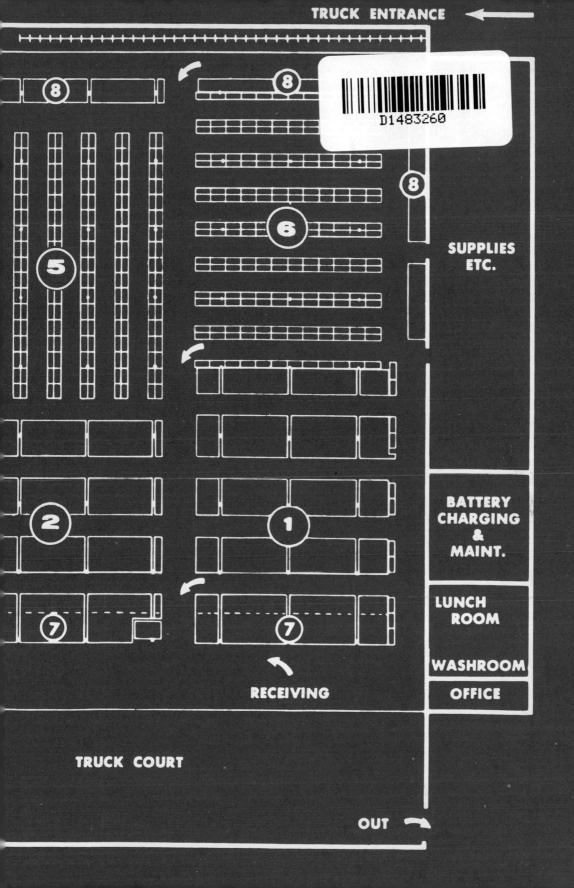

Understanding Today's Food Warehouse

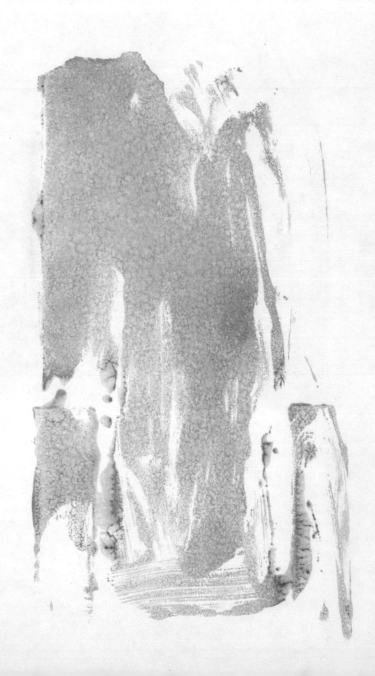

Understanding Today's Food Warehouse

S. O. Kaylin

Chain Store Age Books
A Division of
Chain Store Publishing Corporation
New York

A special edition of this book, entitled "Food Warehousing and Transportation," has been prepared for the Cornell University Home Study Program.

Acknowledgments

As the first textbook on food distribution centers, this work could not have been written without the cooperation of numerous practitioners in the field who made information freely available to the author, offered valuable suggestions on the manuscript, and welcomed first-hand investigation of their distribution centers.

The author is particularly indebted to: *David N. Cybul*, AIA, architect and engineer, who supplied essential information on many subjects and whose extensive experience in designing perishables facilities was freely placed at the author's disposal; *Lloyd W. Moseley*, vice president, The Grand Union Company, whose assistance and encouragement in the early stages of planning are gratefully acknowledged; *F. L. Spreyer*, executive vice president, Jewel Companies, Inc., who advised the author on numerous problems and whose special assistance was invaluable; and *Wallace N. Flint*, executive vice president, National Association of Food Chains, who reviewed the manuscript and wrote the introduction.

Special recognition is due the following experts who contributed valuable information and reviewed major portions of the final manuscript: *Sidney H. Kirkpatrick*, director of warehousing and transportation, Acme Markets, Inc.; *John M. Alexander*, vice president, Certified Grocers of California, Ltd.; *Arnold Cohen*, vice president, Food Fair Stores, Inc.; *R. L. Renne*, director of distribution, The Grand Union Company; *Sidney Kom*, food distribution center consultant and engineer, whose plan for the Waldbaum distribution center layout, Garden City, New York, is reproduced in the end papers; and *Bert L. Thomas*, president, Winn-Dixie Stores, Inc.

This book could not have been written without the assistance of many members of the Chain Store Age organization. A special word of thanks goes to: *Marilyn Greenbaum*, administrative assistant to the editorial director, who edited the manuscript and provided many practical suggestions on the organization and mode of presentation; and *David Lighthall*, editor, Supermarket Editions, who provided wise counsel through every stage of the development of the book. Additionally, the contribution of *Gene A. German*, food distribution specialist, Cornell University, who devoted considerable time and energy to reviewing the entire manuscript and making many valuable suggestions, is gratefully acknowledged.

Other important contributors to this work are:

Thomas King, production manager
Alpha-Beta Stores

Dr. John Allen, director, merchandising
Cholm G. Houghton, director, membership
American Meat Institute

A. B. Gebben
American Sanitation Institute

Richard C. Holderness, senior vice president
Robert Walz, warehouse superintendent
Keith Hall, ass't. warehouse superintendent
Charles Bemis, transportation superintendent
Certified Grocers of California, Ltd.

Louis Karney, Western editor
Chain Store Age

H. M. Thornton, general warehouse and transportation manager
Colonial Stores, Inc.

Dr. Earl H. Brown, professor
Food Distribution Management
Cornell University

Albert Daitch, director, dairy division
Daitch Crystal Dairies, Inc.

G. C. Ensslin, marketing division
Digitronics Corp.

Alvin Dobbin, director of distribution
Giant Food, Inc.

H. G. Semken, director of data processing
The Grand Union Company

The National Bakery Division
The Great Atlantic & Pacific Tea Co.

Data Processing Division
International Business Machines Corp.

Ervin Brinkman, warehouse manager
P. J. Murphy
Jewel Companies, Inc.

Wendell M. Stewart, vice president
A. T. Kearney & Co., Inc.

J. W. Woods, director of distribution
The Kroger Co.

D. P. Henderson, general superintendent of distribution
Loblaw, Inc.

John M. Updegraph, principal
McKinsey & Company

Clarence Adamy, president
National Association of Food Chains

D. A. Barnes, manager, food store systems
The National Cash Register Company

James E. Colloton, vice president, warehousing and transportation
National Tea Co.

William Van Loan, vice president
North American Equipment Co.

Robert Basist, vice president, distribution
The Oshawa Wholesale Ltd.

Thomas Mason, superintendent of warehouses and transportation
Norman C. Peterson, controller
Ralphs Grocery Co.

Keith H. Eno, warehouse operations manager (Landover, Md.)
Don M. Peckham, meat specialist
R. L. Rickenbacher, manager, truck operations
Safeway Stores, Inc.

Distribution Center Staff
Super Valu Stores, Inc.

Gary Lee, produce warehouse manager
Bill Madison, delicatessen kitchen manager
Von's Grocery Co.

Robert F. Weis, vice president
Weis Markets, Inc.

R. M. Winslow, management consultant

And last but not least, the late George A. Ramlose, warehouse engineer of Boston, Mass., who first awakened the author's interest in food distribution centers more than 25 years ago and over the years further stimulated his interest in the field.

S. O. Kaylin

New York, N. Y.
January, 1968

Contents

List of Exhibits

List of Tables

Introduction

Wallace N. Flint
Executive Vice President
National Association of Food Chains

All costs of growing, processing, transporting, handling, and sell-ing food are ultimately paid for by the consumer. Keeping these costs as low as possible is a competitive necessity in the food industry. The efficient operation of a food distribution center substantially strength-ens a food company's ability to achieve this goal.

The objective of a food distribution center is to insure a steady, efficient flow of merchandise to the stores it serves. Inadequate or un-balanced supplies mean lost sales and profits. Over-supply is costly and can reduce a company's ability to maintain competitive prices. Thus, only by regulating the flow of merchandise can a food company achieve the highest return on its investment while charging the lowest possible prices.

This book shows how the modern food distribution center achieves its goal. It relates the efficient operation of the distribution center to the efficient operation of the stores it serves.

An understanding of the total process of the distribution of food is essential to anyone who plans a career in the food industry. A suc-cessful career can no longer be based solely on the trial-and-error accumulation of information that served pioneer operators and man-agers so well during the formative years of the modern supermarket.

Although no substitute exists for practical experience, it has be-come increasingly clear that experience must be supplemented by formal study of the complex interconnection of all aspects of the food distribution process.

The broadest target for improvement in food distribution lies in the area of interdependence of producer, shipper, manufacturer, proc-essor, broker, carrier, terminal receiver, distribution center, retail outlet and, most of all, the consumer.

Warehousing and transportation form essential links in that total process. An understanding of how food is distributed speedily and economically is central to an understanding of supermarket operation.

That is why the National Association of Food Chains is happy to see the development of the first textbook on food warehousing and transportation. The author, S. O. Kaylin, editor of the Executives Edition of *Chain Store Age,* has participated in NAFC Warehousing and Transportation Clinics for many years and has written extensively on distribution problems. With the active aid and encouragement of supermarket industry specialists, he undertook to collect an enormous amount of information on the subject.

An understanding of modern food distribution center operation requires a knowledge of space control, cost control, merchandise movement, equipment performance, transportation costs, data processing, personnel relations, and public relations, all of which are dealt with in this book. Anyone who seriously intends to pursue a career in any phase of the food distribution field will profit by studying its pages.

Washington, D. C.

1
THE MODERN FOOD DISTRIBUTION CENTER AND ITS FUNCTIONS

The modern food distribution center serves a vital purpose in the complex process of bringing fresh, wholesome food from the farm, range, and processing plant to the table of the consumer at the lowest possible cost.

Items that move through food distribution centers account for 50 percent of the sales volume of food stores affiliated with corporate, voluntary, and cooperative chains in both the United States and Canada. About thirty billion dollars worth of dry groceries, meats, produce, frozen foods, dairy and delicatessen items, non-foods, and company-manufactured baked goods flow through those distribution centers in a single year.

A *distribution center's* *primary responsibility*

The primary responsibility of a distribution center is to serve a group of stores by supplying a steady flow of food and non-food products in the quantities needed at the times when they are needed.

Every supermarket receives a significant amount of its merchandise from a distribution center. Most corporate chains operate their own distribution centers, although some are served in whole or in part by distribution centers operated by voluntary or cooperative organizations for their members.

A distribution center operated as a voluntary wholesaler serves a group of stores that advertise and identify themselves under a common name. The stores are independently owned and have no ownership of the distribution center.

A distribution center operated by a cooperative group is owned by the stores it serves.

Voluntary group wholesalers have traditionally supplied their affiliated stores with services such as store location and development, accounting, promotion, and supervision. In recent years, the cooperative wholesaling groups have expanded their activities to include similar services.

Unaffiliated stores deal with one or more general wholesalers operating distribution centers that supply merchandise but provide very few additional services.

How the distribution center benefits the stores

The principal function of a distribution center is to consolidate shipments. The distribution center receives a large quantity of each item and combines smaller quantities of many items into a single shipment for each store. Thus, through a distribution center, a store receives a single large delivery of many items, instead of numerous small deliveries.

By delivering consolidated shipments on a regularly scheduled basis, a food distribution center assures an even flow of merchandise to the stores. Because stores know when to expect deliveries, they are able to plan the work schedules of personnel who receive the merchandise. In addition, the stores' tasks of checking incoming merchandise and processing invoices are simplified, compared with the tasks of checking many small individual shipments and processing invoices from direct suppliers.

Because buyers at food distribution centers purchase merchandise in large quantities for distribution to a large number of stores, they gain the benefits of quantity purchase discounts. In addition, the large amount of storage space available in a distribution center permits buyers to take advantage of low market prices for seasonally available merchandise, which the center ships to stores as needed.

Major activities of a distribution center

Whether operated by corporate chains, voluntary or cooperative wholesaling groups, all food distribution centers fulfill their primary responsibility of serving groups of stores by engaging in the following activities:

1. *Receiving*. Incoming merchandise is removed from rail cars and trucks, checked to determine whether the quantities delivered conform with the bills of lading, and inspected to determine whether it conforms with specifications.

2. *Storage*. Merchandise is moved to assigned areas, where it is held until needed.

3. *Order selection*. Merchandise is assembled to fill the orders of individual stores.

4. *Shipping*. Store orders are placed on over-the-road vehicles, transported to their destinations, and delivered.

Inventory control plays an important part in the operation of a food distribution center. Accurate records must be maintained, indicating in specific detail merchandise on order, merchandise in transit to the distribution center, merchandise in the inventory of the distribution center, and merchandise moved out of the center. Additional records are maintained to indicate the rate of merchandise movement, the locations of merchandise within the distribution center, and the retail and cost prices, gross margins, weights, and cubic measurements of the merchandise.

In addition to these major activities, some distribution centers engage in the additional activity of "processing." The term processing is used broadly to include several types of activities: freezing, cooking, baking, cutting, slicing, weighing, prepricing, prepackaging, and sorting. The extent to which an individual food distribution center engages in these activities depends on whether it can justify them economically.

Handling dry groceries

In the past, many food distribution centers were in reality dry groceries warehouses. Only minor attention was paid to the many other functions that are now assuming great importance.

Today, corporate, voluntary, and cooperative organizations throughout the United States and Canada are concentrating on finding new ways of putting distribution centers to profitable use. Consequently, the dry groceries handling operation is easily taken for granted and its basic role in the operation of a food distribution center is easily overlooked.

In both tonnage and dollar volume of merchandise handled, the distribution of dry groceries outstrips in importance all other functions performed by a food distribution center. A dry groceries operation that is planned and run efficiently can alone justify establishing a distribution facility. Furthermore, it can provide an economic base on which additional operations may be established.

Effect of changing marketing patterns

Traditionally, the dry groceries warehouse was set up to handle fast-moving and moderately fast-moving items. Slow-moving merchandise was usually ordered for delivery directly to the stores. Thus, the warehouse dealt primarily with items that moved in large units at fairly high velocity, and decisions concerning which items to distribute through the warehouse could be made with relatively little difficulty. (Some fast-moving items such as bread and milk are traditionally delivered to stores direct from where they are processed to maintain freshness and avoid double handling.)

Today, the marketing pattern has changed. Because of the proliferation of items, sizes, packages, colors, and brands, consumers now enjoy a wide range of choice. Faced with many possible selections, consumers are distributing their dollars more broadly than in the past. The result is that relatively few items can qualify as fast movers today.

The number of dry groceries items handled in a typical supermarket has increased sharply. A recent study by the Super Market Institute reveals that typical supermarkets today handle 5,000 dry groceries items; three years ago, they stocked 4,700 dry groceries items; six years ago, they stocked 4,300 items.[1]

The impact of new products and broader assortments has been felt by store operators and managers everywhere. Space must be found for more and more new items as established products are continually being re-evaluated to determine how many facings they should get and how much inventory should be carried on each item.

Space "squeeze" at the distribution center

In handling dry groceries, the food distribution center faces essentially the same problems that confront the supermarket. Apart from obvious examples such as soaps and tissues, which are now produced in varied colors, patterns, sizes, or scents, many staple lines have shown large increases in the numbers of items offered for sale. Canned peas, for example, now make up a 17-line listing on one company's order sheet. Sizes for the large family, the medium-sized family, and the two-person family are stocked in a variety of brands, including private-label items. That listing does not include variations of canned peas such as canned peas with pearl onions or mushrooms.

Need for continual item analysis

Today's distribution center planner, therefore, faces a more difficult

[1] *The Super Market Industry Speaks—1966*, Super Market Institute, Chicago.

job of space allocation, organization of the order-selection function, and transportation than he did in the past. In consultation with merchandisers and buyers, he must continually analyze the movement of items to determine what to include in inventory and what to exclude. Items whose sales volume and velocity may not justify handling through a food distribution center might be handled more efficiently on a direct store delivery basis.

In any case, the function of handling dry groceries continues to be a basic responsibility of the distribution center. It is the first operation considered when a distribution center is planned.

Handling non-foods

Many non-edible products, such as soaps, paper goods, tobacco products and cleansers, are generally classified as "dry groceries" because they have been sold traditionally through food stores. Other non-edible products, relatively new in food stores, such as kitchenware, toys, health and beauty aids, and apparel, are generally classified as "non-foods." Retail food organizations do not always agree on which items should be classified as "non-foods" and which should be classified as "dry groceries."

Many non-food items are available from rack jobbers who deliver directly to stores and are responsible for merchandising and store display.

If a company incorporates non-foods lines into its standard mix of dry groceries merchandise at its distribution center, it may encounter some difficulties because many non-foods cannot be handled in the same way as dry groceries are handled.

Handling frozen foods

Frozen foods warehousing is an additional function assumed by an increasing number of food distribution centers. Temperature control and stock rotation are key factors in the proper handling of frozen foods, and special facilities are required. In the handling of such foods, a high degree of mechanization (sometimes mistakenly called "automation") may be used. As units of merchandise tend to be uniform in size and light in weight, frozen foods are ideally suited to handling with conveyors.

The decision as to whether to include the frozen foods handling function in a food distribution center is based on an analysis of the following factors:

1. Services that can be performed by an existing frozen foods wholesaler.
2. Feasibility of investing in the mechanical equipment and the

insulated structure or area required for maximum efficiency.

3. Transportation equipment required.

Handling fresh meats

In planning a modern distribution center, consideration is usually given to establishing a meat handling facility. That facility may be a transfer station where packers' cuts are received, inspected for weight and quality, selected for shipment, and transported to stores. The meat facility may engage in additional activities such as the aging of meat and the slicing, weighing, prepricing, and prepackaging of luncheon meats.

The meat warehouse may go a step further and cut meats into primal cuts. A few companies have set up meat warehouses as complete central processing plants where primal cuts are produced and then broken into retail cuts that are weighed, prepriced, and prepackaged.

Although most companies are not ready today to establish complete central meat plants, many are attempting to determine whether it will be economically feasible to do so in the near future.

Experts in meat distribution believe the trend will run strongly toward central processing of meats into retail cuts, or at the very least, primal cuts. For that reason, any company planning to add a meat facility to its food distribution center should consider building a distribution center that may be expanded into a complete central meat plant when it becomes economically feasible to operate one. In areas where conditions permit the trend to develop, a company may find itself under an economic disadvantage if it has not made provision for expanding into the field of central meat processing in the relatively near future.

Handling produce

The produce handling function is generally accepted as an integral part of the modern food distribution center.

Regional, climatic, transportation, and merchandising factors vary from company to company, however, and affect the methods used to handle fresh fruits and vegetables.

Handling dairy and delicatessen

Dairy products and delicatessen items are related in so far as handling procedures are concerned. Slicing, wrapping, weighing, prepricing, prepackaging, and some manufacturing are involved in the handling of both groups of items. When these activities are performed in a food distribution center, they are generally combined under a single supervisor. Distribution and merchandising executives usually decide jointly whether the activities will be performed at the distribution center or in individual stores. Because of economies available in assembly-line operation, the trend is running strongly toward centralization of these activities. In addition, considerable specialized knowledge is needed to operate a profitable dairy-delicatessen processing facility, and the employment of specialists is more economical in a single central plant than in many individual stores.

Handling baked goods

Company-produced baked goods, in addition to being highly profitable, will also attract customers to a store. Many retail food companies confine their central baking operations to the production of bread and perhaps rolls. Others prepare baked goods that may be finished in the stores or in the homes of consumers. Still others prepare complete lines of baked goods.

Since baked goods are available from outside sources, it is possible to defer a decision to include a partial or complete baking facility in a new distribution center. If land is available, a bakery facility may be built if later investigation proves it is desirable.

Merchandise control, forecasting, and buying

A modern food distribution center is more than a merchandise-handling facility. Merchandise control, forecasting, and buying are intimately related to the distribution center's activities. Such activities are best performed when they are housed in close proximity to the areas where the merchandise itself is handled. Merchandisers, buyers, and data processing personnel generally maintain their offices within the food distribution center, rather than at a point remote from the center.

Transportation

Finally, the entire transportation operation is considered in planning a food distribution center. In its broadest sense, "transportation" includes:

1. Administration of methods of shipping merchandise from suppliers to the distribution center.
2. Internal movement of merchandise from receiving docks to storage and from loading docks to vehicles.
3. Purchasing, operating, maintaining, and dispatching vehicles.
4. Training and supervising transportation employees.
5. Keeping records and making analyses of these records to guide a company in the efficient operation of the transportation department.

Planning ahead

It is obvious that today's distribution center is no longer the simple dry groceries warehouse of the past. The functions it is capable of performing are numerous. It is only after all of the functions have been analyzed, and specific operations have been accepted or rejected, that the next step in planning a center can be taken. That step is to determine when it becomes economically feasible to establish a distribution center.

2 DETERMINING THE ECONOMIC FEASIBILITY OF A DISTRIBUTION CENTER

The problem of determining when it is economically feasible for a new distribution center to be established arises whenever existing central facilities are likely to become inadequate.

The establishment of a new distribution center is considered when an existing center, operated by a general line wholesaler, a corporate chain, or a voluntary or cooperative wholesaling group, is too small to serve a growing number of stores or to fill the needs of existing stores whose sales volume is increasing. As an alternative to setting up an additional new distribution center, an existing center may be expanded or replaced.

If a corporate chain which obtains its dry groceries through the distribution center of a general line wholesaler or as a member of an affiliated group becomes large enough, it may consider building and operating its own distribution center.

Most corporate food chains do operate their own distribution centers. A Cornell University study of 60 corporate food chains indicated that all but seven operated their own centers. Of the seven, six had 1965 sales of less than $20,000,000 and one had 1965 sales of more than $100,000,000.[1]

According to one report, a dry groceries distribution center can be operated advantageously when the value of the merchandise shipped by the center is as low as $6,000,000 to $8,000,000 annually.[2]

Although the volume of merchandise currently being shipped is an important criterion in determining whether to build a new distribution center, or to replace or expand an existing distribution center, the following factors must also be considered:

1. *Location of the stores.* The distribution center should be centrally located, so that it is within reasonable distance from the stores it will serve. A corporate chain with an annual sales volume well over $15,000,000, for example, may not find it economically feasible to operate its own distribution center if its stores are widely scattered. For the center to be economically feasible, the cost of transportation, when added to the expense of operating the distribution center itself, should result in a delivered cost of merchandise that is less than, or no more than, the delivered cost of goods from other sources.

2. *Anticipated future volume.* The expansion program within the area to be served must be studied to determine whether future volume will be sufficient to justify establishing a distribution center. Even though current volume may not be high enough to warrant the building of a center, anticipated volume increases may justify it.

A distribution center is always planned to handle more merchandise than is distributed at the time the center begins operations. Usually, a distribution center is planned to meet store demand projected for five or six years after the date the center is opened. If that were not done, it would quickly become inadequate.

Several years may elapse between the initial decision to build and the actual beginning of operations in the center. Time is needed for acquiring land, zoning, and financing; for planning the building and the systems that will be installed; for construction and the installation of equipment; and for the recruiting, hiring, and training of employees. Still more time is needed to stock the distribution center and to go through "shakedown" operations. Because of the length of time needed for planning and building, a distribution center is seldom built to meet the conditions that exist when planning begins. The anticipated rate of growth in sales volume and in number of stores to be served is, therefore, an important factor in the final decision.

[1] From unpublished data collected in connection with the *1965-1966 Operating Results of Food Chains*, by Wendell Earle and John Sheehan, Cornell University.
[2] *Marketing Research Report No. 348*, U.S. Department of Agriculture, 1959.

Analysis of costs

Once the demand for a distribution center has been determined, the actual cost of building and operating the center must be estimated.

The cost of constructing, equipping, and operating a modern food distribution center is, of course, the major factor in deciding whether to build.

The following simplified hypothetical case is presented to illustrate how annual costs of occupancy and operation may be estimated. The costs of occupancy and operation in the example are based on a series of assumptions. It should be stressed that the costs are dependent on many factors, including extent of site development required, cost of raw land, cost of engineering and architectural services, cost of construction labor and materials, specifications for construction, and the type of materials handling equipment specified. The average distance of stores from the site, frequency of deliveries, labor rates, taxes, cost of bringing utility services to the site, insurance costs, mix of merchandise to be handled, and cost of fees connected with finding, purchasing, and zoning the land will vary. Any estimate of costs for a specific proposed distribution center must therefore be made in relation to the specific conditions under which the facility will be built and operated.

A hypothetical example

The figures which follow apply to a 200,000 square foot facility handling dry groceries only.[3]

1. *Land.* Fifteen acres of land are required. At $20,000 an acre, the cost of land will be $300,000. Land area is slightly more than three times the area of the building to be constructed, to allow for truck yards, rail spurs, parking, auxiliary structures, and future expansion. Assuming the land will be rented rather than purchased, a fair annual rental charge is 8 percent of the land cost, or $24,000.

2. *Building.* If the 200,000 square foot building costs $6.50 a square foot to construct, the building cost is $1,300,000. Assuming that the building is rented, a fair annual rental charge is 1/9 of the construction cost, or approximately $145,000.

3. *Equipment.* The cost of equipping the facility is $210,000. A fair annual rental cost for the equipment is determined by charging 1/7 of the initial cost, or $30,000.

4. *Merchandise handling.* Dry groceries move into, and out of, the

[3] All figures used in the example were derived from summary reports of management clinics on warehousing and transportation published by the National Association of Food Chains for 1954, 1956, 1959, 1963 and 1965, and from the *1964-65 Operating Results of Food Chains,* Cornell University, 1965. Adjustments were made after consultation with practitioners in the distribution center field.

distribution center at a rate of 1.5 tons per man-hour, at an hourly wage rate of $3.25, including fringe benefits. It would therefore cost approximately $2.17 for the labor to move one ton ($3.25 per man-hour ÷ 1.5 tons per man-hour). Assume that the facility will serve 100 stores, delivering an average of 1,465 tons per store per year. Thus, annual shipments to stores will total 146,500 tons (1,465 tons per store × 100 stores). For every ton that moves out of the facility, one ton must be moved in, so that the total annual tonnage handled will be 293,000 tons (146,500 tons × 2). The handling of 293,000 tons per year at $2.17 per ton costs a total of approximately $636,000 per year (293,000 tons × $2.17).

5. *Shipping.* The average distance of stores from the distribution center is 60 miles, and the stores receive dry groceries deliveries on the average of twice a week. Weekly round-trip mileage per store will be 240 miles (120 miles round trip × 2). Allowing for contingencies such as detours, assume that total weekly mileage per store is 250 miles, or 13,000 miles per year (250 miles × 52 weeks). Total annual mileage for 100 stores is 1,300,000 miles (13,000 miles per store × 100 stores). At an average of 35 cents a mile, transportation will cost $455,000 annually. This computation is based on the assumption that 400,000 miles entail city driving, in slow-moving traffic with many stops, at 55 cents a mile, and that 900,000 miles entail over-the-road driving at 26 cents a mile.

6. *Backhauls.* Backhauls of merchandise from suppliers to the food distribution center cost $18,000 a year in drivers' time and excess mileage. In the long run money is saved by backhauls, but the cost of the backhaul operation must be listed as an expense.

7. *Taxes.* Real estate and property taxes on the building, equipment, and inventory total $140,000 a year.

8. *Maintenance, repairs, and related costs.* Maintenance and repairs (other than those for over-the-road vehicles, included in transportation cost), insurance, security, light, heat, and power total $58,000 a year.

9. *Supervision.* Salaries and fringe benefits for the supervisory force cost $50,000 a year.

10. *Data processing.* Data processing equipment and personnel are used by the distribution center for record keeping, inventory control and research purposes. A fair pro rata charge to the distribution center for data processing is $50,000 a year.

11. *Supplies.* Supplies such as printed forms, tags, cleaning materials, and office materials cost $25,000 a year.

12. *Other costs.* Three percent of the total annual cost is allocated for certain administrative expenses, uneven work loads, partial subsidization of a cafeteria, and use of some space for nondistribution

center activities. The total of items 1 through 11 is $1,631,000 in annual expense. Three percent of that amount is approximately $49,000 ($1,631,000 × .03).

Table 1 summarizes the costs of occupancy and operation.

Table 1. Annual Costs of Occupancy and Operation of a 200,000 Square Foot Dry Groceries Distribution Center to Serve 100 Supermarkets

1. Rental of land	$ 24,000
2. Rental of building	145,000
3. Rental of equipment	30,000
4. Merchandise handling	636,000
5. Shipping	455,000
6. Backhauls	18,000
7. Taxes	140,000
8. Maintenance, repairs, insurance, security, light, heat and power	58,000
9. Supervision	50,000
10. Data processing	50,000
11. Supplies	25,000
Total of items 1 through 11	$1,631,000
12. Add 3% to total cost for other expenses	49,000
Grand total	$1,680,000

Interpreting the figures

At approximately $462 a ton, 146,500 tons have a retail value of $67,680,000. This is the dollar value of the dry groceries shipped annually to the 100 stores in our example.

The cost of distributing this merchandise is figured as a percentage of the value of the goods shipped. Since the total cost of operating the food distribution center, including transportation, is $1,680,000 annually, the distribution cost is 2.48 percent of $67,680,000, the value of the goods shipped. This basic figure, 2.48 percent, will help to determine whether the company should establish a distribution center.

Savings on merchandise handled through the distribution center should be equal to or greater than the cost of operating the center. In the example outlined above, if the company is obtaining its dry groceries through a wholesaler's distribution center, it compares the total store-door cost of merchandise under its present arrangement with what the cost would be if it were to set up its own center.

If substantially more than 2.48 percent of the value of the goods shipped is reflected in the total store-door cost, the company will decide to set up its own distribution center. If substantially less than 2.48 percent of the value of the goods shipped is reflected in the total store-door cost, the company will decide not to set up its own distribution center. If, however, the total store-door cost will be the same under either arrangement, the company may nevertheless decide to set up its own center because of several additional benefits it may gain. Those benefits include (1) control of both the wholesale and the retail distribution operations and (2) ability to expand its sales volume without depending on a wholesaler's distribution center to adjust to its expanding requirements.

Estimating costs for other functions

Up to this point, only the dry groceries operation has been considered. The costs of occupying and operating facilities to handle fresh meats, dairy and delicatessen, frozen foods, baked goods, produce, and non-foods differ from the costs of handling dry groceries. For that reason, the costs relating to these functions must be analyzed separately to determine whether it is economically feasible to incorporate them into a distribution center.

The method of making the analyses, however, is the same as the method followed in the hypothetical example given for dry groceries.

If a company operates one or more distribution centers it may eventually have to decide whether to establish still another distribution center to serve its expanding needs. Again, the cost analysis for setting up and operating an additional distribution center is the same as that outlined in the example above.

Planning ahead

Once the decision to build a food distribution center has been made and the functions it will perform have been determined, the location of the facility must next be planned.

Glossary

A corporate food chain *is a group of retail stores owned and operated by a corporation under a single corporate name and management. The corporate chain centralizes its buying and distributes merchandise to its stores through its own distribution center. Frequently smaller chains use the distribution center facilities of a voluntary or cooperative group with which they may be affiliated.*

Affiliated groups or affiliated wholesalers *are organizations such as IGA, Red & White and Shop Rite. These organizations are comprised of independently owned stores that affiliate themselves with a wholesaler in order to take advantage of the benefits of group buying and advertising.*

The voluntary group wholesaler *is an affiliated wholesaler who organizes independent retailers under a group store identification.*

The cooperative group wholesaler *is also an affiliated wholesaler, organized by independent retailers who band together to operate a wholly owned wholesale distribution center.*

3
LOCATING
A DISTRIBUTION CENTER

The entire process of site selection is designed to achieve a single purpose: to obtain a location at which the day-by-day operation of a food distribution center may be carried on at the lowest possible cost consistent with providing satisfactory service to the affiliated stores. It is a complex task that leads to millions of dollars in capital expenditures and operating costs. A company must evaluate prospective sites in relation to land cost, accessibility, future growth of stores, and many other factors.

The general geographical area

The first major location decision a company must make involves the selection of a general geographical area. To provide regular, dependable service at a reasonable cost, the distribution center must be close to the stores. If deliveries are delayed, stores will be unable to meet the needs of their customers. Moreover, if long distances separate the distribution center from the stores, valuable trucking equipment will be tied up for too much time in relation to the value of the loads carried. If delivery service costs too much, stores will have to pass along the higher costs to their customers and their competitive positions will be adversely affected.

For these reasons, 150 miles is about as far as groceries may be hauled by truck at acceptable ratios of expense to total volume. In addition, the Interstate Commerce Commission limits truck operation by one man to approximately 150 miles one way or 300 miles round trip.

Consequently, except for a few rare and unusual situations, food distribution centers are planned to serve territories that are no more than 150 miles in all directions from the site. Many distribution centers are set up to serve stores located at maximum distances of 100, 75, or even 50 miles, but they are ready to serve growing territories if necessary.

If a company operates more than one distribution center, the locations should be far enough away from one another for maximum effective and efficient geographical coverage. Thus, a new distribution center would usually be located a minimum of 300 miles from a company's existing distribution center, so that the 150 mile practicable truck-service radius is protected.

Locating to serve a cluster of stores

The general geographical location for a distribution center is relatively easy to determine when a concentrated group of stores is served. When stores are located within short distances of one another, as they are in densely populated metropolitan areas, the basic consideration for the location of the center is that it be reasonably close to most of the stores.

Ideally, the site selected should be in the center of the store cluster so that trucks fanning out from the distribution center will have to cover only the shortest possible distances. The ideal central location, however, is seldom available in a thickly populated area. In many cases, a location as close as possible to most of the stores will be satisfactory.

Locating to serve scattered stores

Selecting a location for a distribution center which will serve widely separated stores in an area that is not densely populated requires a major study of the entire geographical area.

In such an area, population growth may be anticipated in the near future. Consequently, one may expect a company to develop additional supermarkets to serve the increasing population.

The problem then becomes one of selecting a location that will serve the existing stores efficiently and will also maintain its efficiency as additional stores are opened in the area. Trained economic analysts, who are skilled in projecting population trends and in suggesting the directions which supermarket expansion should take, are employed by larger companies or are available as consultants.

The location selected for a distribution center serving widely scattered stores should be as close as is practicable to the center of the area to be served, and the fact that future stores as well as existing ones will be serviced from the center should be kept in mind.

Major factors in site selection

Once the general geographical area has been selected, specific sites should be considered. The specific location for a food distribution center is selected on the basis of many factors. The most important factors that will be considered are:

1. Land cost
2. Rail facilities
3. Access to good roads
4. Availability of employees
5. Utilities
6. Tax rates
7. Zoning restrictions
8. Accessibility to an airfield
9. Concentration of air pollution
10. Shape of the site
11. Availability of public transportation
12. Community resources
13. Public acceptance of the center
14. Provision for expansion

Land cost

The cost of land must always be weighed against other factors that are equally important in the selection of a site for a food distribution center. A site selected solely because the land cost is relatively low might turn out to be a very expensive investment in the long run.

For example, one 15-acre site may cost only $150,000, while another 15-acre site may cost $600,000. If the first site is selected, the saving in land cost is $450,000.

However, to serve 100 stores from the first site may require an annual cost of $500,000 for transportation, because the average distance of the stores from the site is great—perhaps 100 miles.

To serve 100 stores from the second site may only require an annual transportation cost of $327,000, because the average distance to the stores is relatively low—perhaps 60 miles.

Therefore, the annual saving in transportation cost from the more expensive site would be $173,000 a year. The additional $450,000 paid for the land would be offset in little more than two and one-half years and the saving in transportation cost would be enjoyed each successive year for perhaps 30 years. Thus, an additional investment of $450,000 to obtain the more desirable second site could conceivably lead to a reduction in net expenses, over 30 years, of $4,740,000.

The selection of a specific location for a food distribution center is therefore never based solely on the cost of the land.

Rail facilities

A major factor in determining the best possible site is the transportation facilities available. These facilities must be adequate if the center is to run efficiently.

Rail receipts at modern food distribution centers usually account for about 40 percent of incoming merchandise. Many companies' rail receipts run from 20 to 40 percent of total incoming merchandise, but in some cases the rate goes as high as 60 percent. In a recent study of 35 distribution centers, 8 received 19 percent or less of their inbound cases by rail, 21 received 20 to 40 percent by rail, and 6 received 41 to 60 percent by rail.[1] The actual percentage of rail receipts is governed by a number of factors, including geographic location of the site in relation to major manufacturing centers, size of the distribution center, and volume of merchandise moved through the center.

Every large food distribution center must, however, have available rail service from at least one major railroad. Moreover, the site should be so located that adequate and frequent switching service is possible. A location within free reciprocal switching limits—permitting rail cars to move freely to where they are needed—is highly desirable. A rail siding is essential.

Access to good roads

Receipt of merchandise by truck accounts for from 60 to 80 percent of incoming goods for most companies.[2] Usually, all of the outgoing merchandise shipped to the stores moves by truck.

The site must therefore be convenient to a major highway network, with adequate access from the site to the highway. Highway toll charges, if any, should be considered as a factor, however minor, in weighing one site against another.

If possible, the site should be located to minimize truck movement through crowded major metropolitan areas. Daily hauls through crowded areas result in low mileage per hour and, consequently, in substantial increases in the operating costs of a distribution center. Moreover, if a company's trucks contribute unnecessarily to traffic

[1] *June 1966 Grocery Distribution Center Efficiency Report*, by Earl Brown and John Sheehan, Cornell University.
[2] *Ibid.*

congestion, public resentment may be aroused and store sales may suffer.

Availability of employees

Dollar differentials cannot always be calculated in comparing the advantages and disadvantages of various sites. For example, a distribution center which is not easily accessible to potential employees is at a disadvantage, although this factor is difficult to assess in dollars and cents.

With a small labor pool available within comfortable traveling distance, a company is not likely to attract the best possible work force. Increased costs caused by this "hidden" factor may mount over the years, so that the distribution center will always be carrying a financial burden it might have avoided in another location. In a metropolitan location, for example, a relatively large labor pool is generally available to a distribution center.

If employees must travel considerable distances in order to work at a distribution center, over the long run the company will have to offer them inducements to do so. Increased costs due to this factor are difficult to measure during the site selection process, but they should be given some weight before a final determination is made, especially because the annual penalty for making a bad decision is multiplied by the number of years the distribution center is in existence.

Utilities

The availability of utility service is an important factor to consider in selecting a site for a distribution center.

A public water main of sufficient size to provide for all foreseeable in-plant uses is highly desirable. This factor assumes increased importance if a considerable amount of processing of perishables is contemplated.

Sufficient water volume and pressure should be available to service a sprinkler system even if one is not to be installed initially, since later experience may require such an installation. If sufficient water volume and pressure are not available, the warehouse planner must estimate the cost of installing standby water service such as tanks and pumps.

The cost of bringing water mains to the property line is sometimes borne by the municipality or a water supply company and sometimes by the property owner. The warehouse planner must determine the facts in the case of each potential site and must calculate the cost, if any, to the company of bringing the mains to the property line.

Accessibility to a public sewer is highly desirable. Private sewage disposal plants are expensive to build and to maintain. They are not as flexible as public sewers in the handling of expanded needs and, in general, are not as satisfactory as public sewers.

If public sewer mains are to be brought to the property line, the warehouse planner must include the expense of doing so in his estimate of costs.

Electric power and telephone service are readily available in most areas. Service is ordinarily brought to the property line at no cost to the owner. The electric power rate schedule, however, should be analyzed to determine whether it is favorable or whether it will result in unusually high costs of operations requiring electric power.

The availability of natural gas is considered highly desirable although not essential. Rates should be investigated to determine whether the use of natural gas will be economically feasible. Growing applications of the "on-site power generation" concept—the use of natural gas to manufacture power at the distribution center and to supply heat which may be used for air conditioning and water heating—makes accessibility to natural gas lines a factor to consider.

Tax rates

Tax rates are important in evaluating the desirability of a site. Taxes represent an unavoidable annual expense, and once a company has committed itself to a site it must be prepared to shoulder its tax burden. Taxes are likely to increase with each passing year and only in very rare individual cases are they ever decreased through reappraisal of the property or readjustment of the tax schedule applying to the specific property. All taxes—city, county, state, real estate, and personal property—must be considered when a site is under evaluation.

Zoning restrictions

Each potential site must be analyzed to determine whether necessary zoning can be secured for the building of a modern distribution center. A piece of property suitable in all respects may have to be rejected because proper zoning may not be forthcoming. While it is possible to arrange for the purchase of land subject to zoning board approval of the site, zoning procedures take time. By the time a company learns that the necessary zoning for the distribution center will not be forthcoming, its alternate choices of land may no longer be available.

Accessibility to an airfield

The travel requirements of the modern businessman make it highly desirable that the site of the distribution center be accessible from commercial airfields. Company officials use airlines more extensively today than in the past. Satisfactory airline connections to and from the site will save valuable traveling time.

In the future, the development of large cargo planes may make it economically feasible to receive an increasing number of perishables by air. Since a distribution center is planned for operation many years into the future, it is wise to consider this factor in selecting a site.

Concentration of air pollution

In metropolitan areas the problem of air pollution poses an increasingly important threat to the operation of plants handling perishables. A site should not be located near chemical plants. It should be accessible to, but at a safe distance from, airfields and high-speed highways. Pollutants in higher-than-acceptable concentrations should not be permitted to penetrate the buildings that house operations such as meat processing. To guard against the effects of polluted air, expensive construction and equipment must be used.

Shape of the site

Another consideration in evaluating a potential site is whether the shape of the land lends itself to the construction of a building with an efficient layout. The layout of the distribution center affects the efficiency of its operation. The shape of the building is affected by the layout and restricted by the shape of the site. A distribution center that must be built in the shape of an L or a U, because of the shape of the site, is generally less efficient than one built in the form of a rectangle. Moreover, under today's conditions, with limited use of automation, a single-floor operation is superior to a multi-floor operation. A planner, then, would seek land on which a single-story, rectangular structure could be built. Provision is usually made, however, for mezzanine or second-story space for office use.

Availability of public transportation

A public transportation system serving the site is highly desirable, as this makes the distribution center accessible to both employees and visitors. The availability of public transportation also helps to reduce the amount of parking space needed for employees' and visitors' cars. Moreover, many employees will be spared the necessity of maintaining more than one car, a factor that may help a company obtain superior workers at going wage rates.

Community resources

The community itself should be evaluated to determine whether it is a desirable place in which to live and work. Will it attract good potential employees? Are changes in political administration likely to result in sweeping changes in the level of public service or in the tax structure? Is the school system satisfactory for the children of employees? Is the community growing? Are other businesses seeking sites in the community? These factors should be examined when a specific site is under consideration.

Public acceptance of the center

Community acceptance is an important factor in evaluating a specific site. It should be ascertained whether public officials and business and community leaders are aggressively soliciting light industry such as a distribution center, or are doubtful about accepting this kind of facility. Acceptance by officials and business and community leaders is highly desirable. Not only does community acceptance speed any rezoning which may be required, but it also assures continuing operations in a cooperative atmosphere. For example, while the existing road pattern may be well suited to the needs of the distribution center, some change may be contemplated by the municipality. If the distribution center has established good relations with local officials, they will undoubtedly consider carefully the needs of the distribution center and keep these needs in mind when contemplating changes in the road pattern.

Just as a supermarket seeks community acceptance by avoiding excessive glare from its parking-lot lighting and by minimizing noise from equipment, so does a food distribution center seek to obtain public acceptance by being a good neighbor. Good will, however, must be established early. Selecting a site in a community that is encouraging light industry is an important early step in building good will.

Provision for expansion

Since the price of the land is usually less important than the savings that accrue because of strategic location, experts suggest that no compromise be made on acquiring the best-located site available.

It is essential that sufficient land be acquired to meet current needs and to provide for future expansion. Many otherwise usable distribution centers have been abandoned because they could not be expanded to meet growing needs.

"Buy more land than you think is needed," advises one experienced distribution center planner. "New functions, which demand land area, are constantly being added to service centers. Furthermore, if a major food distribution center is built, other industry is attracted to the developed area. If you end up with more land than you need, the resale value is usually much higher than the purchase price plus carrying charges."

"The land itself," he emphasizes, "is ordinarily the cheapest part of the warehouse, no matter how expensive the real estate seems to be."

A poorly selected site can drain a company's profits year after year and can hinder a company's growth. A well-selected site, however, can contribute to the profits of every store served and can be of major assistance in permitting a company to serve the expanding needs of its trading area.

DETERMINING THE SIZE
OF A DISTRIBUTION CENTER

The size of a food distribution center is determined by the quantity of merchandise that must be handled by the center to adequately serve the needs of the stores.

To determine how much merchandise will be handled, the distribution center planner obtains from each merchandising department an informed estimate of the quantity of every item for which space must be allocated and of the average length of time each item will be held in the warehouse inventory. These estimates are based on a careful analysis of records of current merchandise movement and an estimate of projected volume. This general procedure is applied to merchandise for all departments of the stores served by the distribution center.

Most distribution centers are built around the dry groceries warehouse. Therefore, dry groceries, including repack items, are analyzed first to determine the size of the facility needed to handle them.

Non-foods are usually included in the analysis of dry groceries requirements, because non-foods are generally handled as part of, or as an adjunct of, a dry groceries operation.

Not every distribution center handles merchandise for the meat, produce, frozen foods, baked goods, and dairy-delicatessen departments. For those that do, the analysis of space needs would be handled in a manner similar to that used for the dry groceries operation.

The relationship between space and volume

Typical relationships between the size of the distribution center and the volume of dry groceries moving through it are indicated in the quarterly *Grocery Distribution Center Efficiency Report*, published by Cornell University with the cooperation of the National Association of Food Chains. Examples taken from the reports of March, June, and September, 1966, illustrate how much space is used to accommodate various quantities of merchandise.

For example, in one four-week period, a large distribution center shipped 29,580 tons of dry groceries to its stores. On an annual basis (29,580 tons × 13 four-week periods), approximately 385,000 tons were shipped from this 506,000 square foot distribution center. By dividing the total space by the number of tons shipped per year (506,000 square feet ÷ 385,000 tons), the number of square feet required to handle one ton shipped per year is obtained. In this case, 1.57 square feet are used for each annual ton shipped.

A random selection of figures for distribution centers included in the reports shows the following:

Square Footage	Tons Shipped Annually	Square Feet Used For One Annual Ton Shipped
506,000	385,000	1.57
246,000	260,000	0.95
200,000	143,500	1.39
195,000	135,000	1.56
187,000	101,000	1.85
170,000	143,500	1.05
135,000	149,500	0.90

As indicated above, the ratio of square feet of distribution center space to annual tons shipped ranges from .90 to 1.85 for seven companies selected at random.

Distribution center experts estimate that a well-run operation initially requires 1.35 square feet of distribution center space for each ton of dry groceries shipped annually. This figure includes space for storage, aisles, docks, equipment rooms, offices, and expansion needs. It also takes into consideration the factors of (1) merchandise turnover, (2) advance large-scale purchasing, (3) service level, and (4) distribution center design. If any of these factors are expected to vary considerably from the norm, space adjustments are made.

Merchandise turnover

The faster merchandise moves in and out of the distribution center, the less space is needed to store the total quantity required to supply stores in the course of a year.

As an extreme example, if 50,000 cases of an item are needed to take care of the annual requirements of 100 stores, and if 50,000 cases are received at the distribution center at one time and shipped to the stores as they are needed, a large amount of space would be required because all 50,000 cases would be in storage in the distribution center at one time. If, however, 5,000 cases were received in each of ten equally spaced shipments during the year, about one-tenth of the space would be required. The rate at which merchandise turns over affects the amount of space needed in a distribution center.

Merchandise turnover is calculated by dividing the total quantity shipped in one year by the average inventory. A weighted average turnover of 19.16 times for dry groceries in distribution centers is reported by food chains whose distribution center activity is charted by Cornell University.[1] Individual companies reported turnover rates falling within the wide range of 9 times to 42 times.

The formula of 1.35 square feet for each ton shipped annually takes into account the total space needed if annual warehouse turnover is at the rate of 15 or 16 times. If a company's turnover rate is higher, correspondingly less space would be needed. If the rate is lower, more space would be needed.

Advance large-scale purchasing

Merchandisers and buyers often decide, on the basis of their experience and their knowledge of market conditions, that certain items should be purchased and stored in large quantities and shipped out to the stores as they are needed. Some items, for example, are available at low prices during the seasons they are harvested. Although they are sold in the stores throughout the year, it may be wise to purchase them in large quantities as soon as they become available; otherwise a company may have to pay much higher prices later. Since the stores would have to pass the increased costs on to their customers, they would be placed in a poor competitive position.

Therefore, a company may decide to purchase and store a large quantity of an item such as canned peaches, shipping the product to the stores only as it is needed. This means, of course, that space must be allocated in the distribution center to items that are to be stored longer than normal periods.

To deal with this situation, a planner lists all the items that are likely to be purchased in quantity to take advantage of low market

[1] *1966 Grocery Distribution Center Efficiency Report,* Cornell University.

prices. He then estimates how long they will be stocked and how much space must be allocated for this purpose over the course of a year.

Because it costs money to buy merchandise in advance and to store it, these costs must be compared with the probable savings achieved by buying when the market price is low. The advantage of having merchandise available when it is needed must also be considered. Buyers and distribution center executives continually seek to balance price advantages against cost factors. On a practical level, they seldom arrive at a complete answer to the problem.

The formula of 1.35 square feet per annual ton shipped takes into account the storage space needed for holding a reasonable quantity of merchandise purchased in advance of needs. If a company's history or its proposed future policy indicates that advance purchases will be substantially greater than is customary in the food field, then the distribution center would have to be proportionately larger.

Steady flow

Because a distribution center's primary responsibility is to supply a steady flow of products to stores in the quantities needed at the times they are needed, distribution centers are designed to hold enough merchandise to fill orders for a very high percentage of the items wanted by the stores.

Occasionally, ordered items are not available at the distribution center because incoming shipments have been delayed or demand has been greater than anticipated. On the whole, however, the formula of 1.35 square feet per annual ton of dry groceries shipped provides enough space to handle merchandise to fill store orders for virtually every item required.

Layout of the distribution center

Based on the estimates he has received from each merchandising department, the planner knows not only the number of items and the turnover rate of every item that will flow through the distribution center, but also the approximate size of each case of merchandise that will be handled. He also knows, from past experience, how many cases of specific merchandise can fit on one pallet and allocates space along the selection line in terms of pallet loads of merchandise.

The speed at which items are selected for orders is affected by the distance between each item on the selection line. The planner therefore tries to compress as many merchandise facings as possible within a given area, so that the selection line will be as short as possible. At the same time, however, merchandise cannot be stacked so high that it becomes difficult to reach.

The allocation of 1.35 square feet of space in the distribution center for each ton of dry groceries shipped annually to stores is based on initially stacking pallets two-high in racks along a portion of the selection line (with a third tier holding reserve stock). As time goes on, and items increase in number, more pallet racks are added to the selection line. Such a plan allows for space to handle both expanded lines and an increased number of stores.

With space requirements for the pallets determined, the distribution center planner must then provide aisle space in which to gain access to the merchandise.

In large distribution centers, aisle space should not exceed 30 percent of total floor area. Smaller structures, with less total inventory,

Exhibit 1. Aisle Space in Relation to Total Area

Areas are exaggerated to illustrate the basic principle.

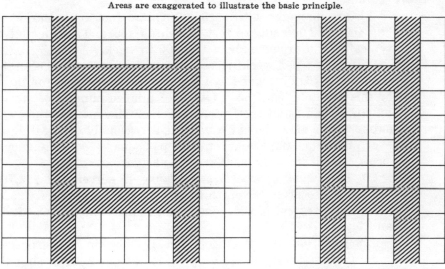

Aisle space in large dry groceries distribution center is 28 percent of total space.

Aisle space in small center is 40 percent of total.

must house the same variety and, consequently, must have the same number of merchandise facings along the selection line as do large structures. Reserve stock stored in one or more rows behind the selection line in larger structures requires no aisle space. The smaller buildings, therefore, require a higher proportion of aisle space (shaded area in Exhibit 1) in relation to total area.

The width of the aisle is determined by the angle at which the pallets are positioned in the selection line. Adequate space must be provided for the maneuvering of fork-lift trucks to gain access to the merchandise. Pallets at 90° angles to the selection aisle necessitate a wider aisle than do pallets placed at 45° angles to the aisle. On the other hand, 90° pallet placement yields more facings per linear foot and more pallets per square foot than does 45° angle storage. This problem is discussed more fully in Chapter 7. It should be noted here, however, that the method of angling pallets along the selection line affects the total space requirement.

Determining the space needs of one store

The following example indicates how the volume of sales generated by one supermarket affects the amount of distribution center space required to service the store. In this example, it is assumed that the factors of merchandise turnover, advance large-scale purchasing, service level, and distribution center design do not deviate from the norm.

Store volume

A store manager with a 15,000 square foot supermarket generally has about 12,000 square feet of selling space. This amount of space, typically, will produce about $30,000 in weekly sales.

Sales of $2 per week per square foot of gross space, or $30,000 a week for a 15,000 square foot supermarket, are used for the purposes of this example. Analysis of sales of a large number of supermarkets by the Urban Land Institute, the Super Market Institute, and others supports the view that $2 a week is a reasonably typical figure. However, individual supermarket sales per square foot may vary, in some cases considerably, from that typical figure.

Of the $30,000 in weekly sales, some 49 percent, or $14,700, would be in dry groceries—everything except meats, produce, frozen foods, dairy-delicatessen, baked goods, and non-foods such as kitchenwares and toys.

About $1,700 of the store's weekly sales in dry groceries would come from items delivered directly to the store, bypassing the distribution center.

In the example, approximately 11.6 percent of dry groceries sales comes from items delivered directly to the store. Estimates vary from 5 to 20 percent for various operations, but 11.6 percent is considered to be a reasonably typical figure by merchandising and distribution executives.

This leaves some $13,000 worth of dry groceries, at retail, to be shipped every week to the store through the distribution center.

Dealing with cases of merchandise

Although the weight of groceries varies considerably from case to case, the average weight of a case may be estimated at 26 pounds, based on figures submitted to Cornell University.[2] About 77 cases generally make up about one ton (2,000 pounds).

Similarly, the retail value of a single case of dry groceries varies; however, $6 can be established as a typical figure. Thus, the typical supermarket would receive an average of 2,167 cases of dry groceries per week ($13,000 ÷ $6 a case = 2,167 cases).

At an average weight of 26 pounds a case, 2,167 cases weigh 56,342 pounds, or 28.17 tons (56,342 pounds ÷ 2,000 pounds = 28.17 tons). The supermarket in our example would therefore receive 28.17 tons of merchandise weekly, or approximately 1,465 tons of dry groceries per year.

Allocating distribution center space

Using the formula of 1.35 square feet of distribution center space for each ton of dry groceries shipped annually, about 1,978 square feet of distribution center space would be allocated for the handling of dry groceries necessary to supply the supermarket in the example (1,465 tons per year × 1.35 square feet per ton shipped annually).

If 100 stores of this size are to be served by the facility, then 197,-800 square feet are required; rounded out, 200,000 square feet would be planned, with 2,000 square feet allocated to each store.

Planning for expansion

When a new distribution center is built, it is purposely made larger than the size required to handle current operations; otherwise, it would be quickly outmoded.

Projected population and income growth in the market areas of the existing stores requires that enough space be provided to handle a reasonable increase in the volume of merchandise flowing through the center.

Moreover, new store construction and expansion of existing stores requires the handling of additional merchandise, while contemplated store closings will reduce the amount of merchandise to be handled. A planned merger or acquisition of another company would obviously have to be taken into consideration. The distribution center planner therefore consults the company's store planning and real estate executives to determine how their programs will affect the need for space. Generally, a distribution center is built large enough to accommodate the stores that will be operated five years after the center goes into operation.

New items that may be added to inventory must also be considered. In the past 12 years, the typical dry groceries warehouse inventory

[2] *March, June, and September, 1966 Grocery Distribution Center Efficiency Report,* Cornell University.

has grown from about 2,000 to 4,500 items, while store inventory has grown to more than 5,000 items (some items are delivered direct to the store, bypassing the warehouse). Just as a supermarket must face the problem of jamming more items into available shelf space, so must the distribution center find ways to solve the problem. Usually, from 5 to 8 percent additional space is provided to accommodate the new items that the center will handle.

Forecasting space requirements, however, is not an exact science. Regardless of the formula used, unanticipated changes are likely to take place.

As an example, the sales forecasts may be exceeded because of a sharp upturn in general or local economic conditions, or the closing of competitive stores; this would result in a demand on the distribution center to supply considerably more merchandise to each store. The opportunity might arise for a company to acquire a group of stores, and the consequent demand on the distribution center may increase overnight. Perhaps a merchandising decision will be taken to develop an entirely new line of bulky non-foods that must be warehoused. Or, new functions such as a salvage operation may be added.

Because unanticipated demands on space are likely, center planners provide for the possibility of expansion at the time the original plans for a new food distribution center are made. The two major forms of expansion provided for are (a) the addition of new functions, and (b) the expansion of existing functions.

Addition of new functions

If new functions are added to those which a distribution center already performs, provision must be made for additional space to house those functions. For example, the original building may have been constructed to accommodate dry groceries, a limited meat operation, and a produce operation. If the company decides to expand its meat operation to the point where retail cuts will be produced for shipment to stores, obviously additional space will be required for that purpose. If frozen foods are to be warehoused, space provisions must likewise be made.

The addition of new functions may be handled by adding on to an existing building, or by building an auxiliary structure. An addition would be made to an existing building if it is desirable to have a common loading dock for the new and existing functions. Also, construction economies are available when a new section is added to an existing building, since central facilities such as heating need not be duplicated.

In any case, to provide for expansion, the approximate land area that will be needed to house the new functions should be blocked out at the time the new distribution center is built.

Expansion of existing functions

If existing functions are to be expanded, an addition to the existing space must be designed to handle the expanded operation. This requires considerable advance preparation.

The key to planning for expansion is to extend the original flow plan smoothly without disturbing the established procedures for handling the merchandise. Provision must therefore be made not only for the necessary amount of additional space, but also for the kind of space—of the proper shape and in the proper location—that will permit maintaining continuity in the materials handling operation.

At the time the original structure is planned, the following factors should be considered as part of advance planning for expansion: (1) availability of adjacent land, (2) wall construction of the original structure, (3) directions in which expansion can take place, and (4) type of foundation to be laid.

Availability of adjacent land. The first step in planning for expansion is the acquisition of adjacent land when the original site is purchased. If rezoning is necessary, the entire acreage should be included in the rezoning application. Soil tests should be made of the adjacent land to determine if the building can be expanded economically in the desired directions. If tests show that a portion of the adjacent land is unsuitable, it may be possible to change the original building plans so that the entire distribution center—the original structure and the expanded structure—can still be accommodated in the land area, with the land unsuitable for building construction being used for a parking area.

Wall construction. The distribution center planner usually designs the structure so that the walls are nonload bearing. Thus, the walls may be conveniently knocked down so that the new section becomes continuous with the old one.

For very large warehouses, however, it is advantageous to retain the walls but to cut doorways in them, since the old walls with fireproof doors act as fire walls to reduce the hazard of fire.

Direction of expansion. For maximum flexibility, the original building should be placed so that it is expandable in all directions if possible. Expansion on two sides may usually be planned with minimum difficulty. The third side, where the truck area is located, presents a more difficult problem, particularly in maintaining operations during the construction period. The fourth side, where the rail siding is located, presents the most difficult expansion problem, but expansion is sometimes indicated on the land across and beyond the track. If this can be done without excessive cost, the plan should be roughed out on the original layout. Planning should also include provisions for additional truck and rail siding space.

Type of foundation. Food distribution centers operate most efficiently in one-floor structures. Administrative functions, however, may be housed in mezzanines or second floors. If a second floor is to be added to accommodate additional office space, planners specify a foundation capable of supporting the additional floors.

In planning the expansion of refrigerated space or conversion from dry to refrigerated space, planners find it advisable to insulate the floors at the time of original construction. The cost of insulating floors originally is much lower than the cost of picking up existing floors and substituting insulated ones.

Some planners lay the foundation of the structure planned for expansion at the time the original foundation is poured. The economy in doing so should be weighed against the advisability of committing a company to a specific expansion area far in advance of the demonstrated need for it.

When to expand

Distribution center planners agree that expansion should take place before a facility becomes so overcrowded that efficiency is impaired. Various methods of measuring efficiency are available. The following table shows productivity figures for dry groceries distribution centers.

Table 2. Measures of Efficiency by Size of Center*

Space Utilized, Square Feet	Number of Centers	Direct Labor per Man-hr.		Total Labor per Man-hr.		Cases per Man-hr.		
		Tons	Cases	Tons	Cases	Unloaded, R.R. Cars	Selected	Loaded
100,000–149,999	5	2.17	160	1.20	88	215	163	424
150,000–199,999	13	1.89	135	1.35	93	222	187	388
200,000–299,999	8	1.89	146	1.34	93	186	147	374
300,000 and over	4	2.00	118	1.18	79	180	195	305

June, 1966 Grocery Distribution Center Efficiency Report, Cornell University.

Distribution executives use figures such as the above as guides in measuring the efficiency of their operations. The figures represent the current experience of many distribution centers. Any significant deviation from the figures may be taken as a signal to investigate whether a specific distribution center requires expansion.

For example, a center in the 200,000 to 299,000 square foot size range may be moving only 1.50 tons per man-hour (direct labor) in comparison with the median of 1.89 tons per man-hour. Further, it may be selecting only 125 cases per man-hour in comparison with 147 cases per man-hour reported as the median for distribution centers in this size group. Investigation of the reasons for these situations may disclose that the distribution center is overcrowded and therefore fork lift trucks are unable to move quickly and directly from receiving dock to storage areas, while, at the same time, selection-line workers are delayed in performing their tasks because space limitations result in shortages of inventory at the point of selection.

When a dry groceries distribution center has slightly less than one square foot (0.90 square foot) per annual ton shipped, expansion is considered necessary. At that point, too little space is available for the work that has to be done, and efficiency suffers to some extent. Warehouse production begins to suffer severely when less than 0.75 square foot per annual ton shipped is used. These estimates are reasonably accurate for large warehouses. Smaller operations require higher ratios of warehouse square footage per annual ton shipped. The biggest space users in a warehouse are aisles and selection lines. As total output grows, the requirements for these areas are reduced as a *percentage* of the additional space needed. Additional space is required primarily to store merchandise, rather than for aisles and selection lines.

Since the planning and the construction of an expanded section take time, operators generally maintain records that show the trend in the use of warehouse space. If the trend is steadily downward in the number of square feet in operation per annual ton, the planning for expansion would begin well in advance of the time that operations actually became inefficient.

The effects of increased volume

The following examples illustrate the effects of increased volume on space in the distribution center.

1. *Additional stores add to volume.* In this hypothetical example, an increase in the number of stores affiliated with a distribution center is considered. These assumptions are made:

(a) To serve 68 stores, a dry groceries warehouse of 135,000 square feet is required if the average annual shipment per store is 1,465 tons. This allows for a ratio of 1.35 square feet per annual ton shipped to be maintained.

Sixty-eight stores, each receiving 1,465 tons annually, account for annual shipments of 99,620 tons (68 stores × 1,465 tons) or, rounded out, 100,000 tons. Calculating space needed at 1.35 square feet per annual ton, total space requirements are 1.35 square feet multiplied by 100,000 tons, or 135,000 square feet.

(b) As stores are added, the average annual shipment per store continues to be 1,465 tons, while the size of the warehouse remains unchanged at 135,000 square feet. (Figures are rounded.)

Number of Stores	Tons Shipped Annually	Square Feet per Annual Ton Shipped
68	100,000	1.35
86	127,000	1.10
102	150,000	0.90
115	169,000	0.80
123	180,000	0.75

Thus, as the original 68 stores increase to 86, the ratio decreases from 1.35 square feet per annual ton to 1.10, and management becomes alerted to the fact that an expanded warehouse should be considered. When 102 stores must be served, the ratio becomes 0.90, and the trend is unmistakable; action should be taken to increase warehouse space before a point of inefficiency in productivity is reached. (See Exhibit 2.) At 115 stores and again at 123 stores the ratio decreases, first to 0.80 and then to 0.75—points that would not have

Exhibit 2. Space Requirements Related to Store Additions

As stores are added, the volume of tonnage shipped increases
and a trend to overcrowding becomes evident.

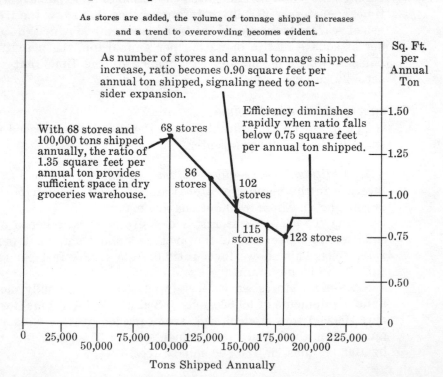

been reached had corrective action been taken before the warehouse operation became too "tight." At these points, errors in selection have probably begun to mount up, increased personnel or increased hours per man have undoubtedly been required, and some stores may have begun to receive deliveries at inconvenient times.

2. *Existing stores increase volume.* Another hypothetical case illustrates what will happen as sales volume increases in existing stores. Each of the 68 stores in the example receives an average of 1,465 tons a year. A 135,000 square foot dry groceries warehouse, operating at 1.35 square feet per annual ton shipped, is adequate to serve the stores. The following figures show what happens when sales increase 10 or 20 percent, while the size of the warehouse remains the same. (Figures are rounded.)

Tons Shipped Annually		Square Feet per
Per Store	68 Stores	Annual Ton Shipped
1,465	100,000	1.35
1,612 (up 10%)	110,000	1.23
1,758 (up 20%)	120,000	1.13

As indicated in the above figures, the distribution center can support a sales increase of 20 percent without reaching the point at which production becomes inefficient.

3. *The combined effect.* A combination of sales increases in existing stores and of additions to the number of stores served could rapidly make the present distribution center inadequate. (See Exhibit 3.)

Assuming that the existing 68 stores enjoyed sales gains of 20 percent at the same time that 55 stores were added (requiring dry groceries shipments at the 1,465-ton level), the result would be:

The 68 stores with shipments of 1,758 annual tons per store, totaling 120,000 tons, plus 55 stores with shipments of 1,465 annual tons per store, totaling 80,600 tons, yield a grand total of 123 stores with annual shipments of 200,600 tons. These stores are served by a 135,000 square foot warehouse. Only 0.673 square foot per annual ton is available for handling the merchandise (135,000 square feet ÷ 200,600 annual tons), a figure well below the point at which operations can be conducted efficiently.

Calculations of this kind, based on records maintained to show trends, indicate the need for an addition to a food distribution center.

The amount of space to add

Once a company has determined that it requires an addition to an existing dry groceries distribution center, it estimates how much additional space it needs. Projections of sales volume per store and of total number of stores to be served obviously form the basis of the estimates.

Exhibit 3. Space Requirements Related to Store Additions and Volume Increases

As stores are added and existing stores enjoy volume increases, space must be added in the distribution center to avoid overcrowding.

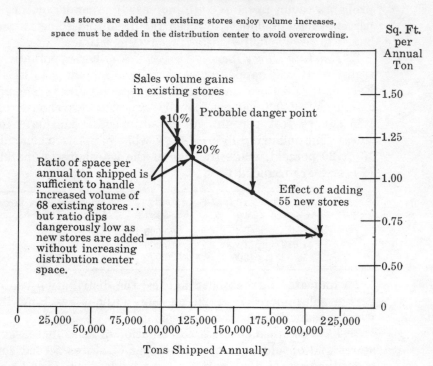

The warehouse planner translates into square footage the estimated increased demand on warehouse service. If 1.35 square feet per annual ton shipped is a reasonably correct figure in the case under his consideration, he would plan to add one square foot of distribution center space for each annual ton estimated to be added to store shipments. The additional space will not maintain the same 1.35 square foot ratio to shipments as does the original space, because aisle space will not be increased in proportion to existing aisle space, service facilities will not have to be added (equipment rooms, employee cafeteria, rest rooms, office space for supervisory personnel), and dock space for receiving and loading will not have to be increased in proportion to existing dock space.

The process of determining the amount of space needed in a distribution center cannot be described completely, however, unless due recognition is given to the fact that space is "alive." As one distribution director puts it, "Space can be used creatively. It can be adjusted to meet changing needs. It is related intimately to the methods used to receive, store, select, and ship the merchandise. Although we plan space to meet a specific set of circumstances, we must also keep firmly in mind the fact that those circumstances are continually changing and that our use of the space must be flexible enough to meet those changed conditions."

DESIGNING
THE DISTRIBUTION CENTER

Although a supermarket planner may work from a standard building plan, he cannot realistically design one supermarket as the exact duplicate of another. Each supermarket has its own design and layout problems.

The shape and topography of the land, the location in relation to access roads, the zoning restrictions on exterior design and refuse disposal, the requirements for parking, and the space available for the receiving dock are some factors that vary considerably from site to site.

Space limitations on future expansion may affect the original design of a supermarket. Whether a store is free standing or part of a shopping center complex is important in planning its design. Finally, a large store cannot be laid out in exactly the same manner as a small store.

The designer of a food distribution center faces similar problems. There is no one method of handling merchandise that can be used in every operation. For this reason, no planner can produce a single, all-purpose layout to be used in all food distribution centers.

Planning the layout

Before deciding on a layout for a specific distribution center, the planner must determine the system that will be used to receive, store, select, and ship merchandise. He estimates the quantity of goods that will be handled by the center and the frequency of merchandise arrival and shipment. He then devises a flow plan to indicate the direction in which merchandise will move from the time it is received to the time it is shipped.

To assess the entire process of getting the merchandise from producer to store door, the following factors must be studied carefully:

1. *Lead time.* The amount of time that will elapse between the placing of orders and the receipt of merchandise is known as "lead time." Calculations of the lead time required for various categories of merchandise help the planner to devise a layout plan that will provide for a smooth flow of goods into and out of the distribution center.

2. *Shipping methods.* The methods used to ship merchandise to the distribution center determine the type of receiving facilities that must be provided for in the layout. The proportion of receipts by rail and by truck must be considered and dock space allocated to each type of receiving procedure. Rail spurs are usually placed to one side of the building, and truck receiving is usually placed on the side adjacent to the rail spur.

A fully enclosed truck-receiving area is often considered desirable. Superior working conditions in all weather, orderly supervision of the stream of traffic, shorter unloading time, and fewer opportunities for pilferage are advantages claimed for the enclosed truck area.

The volume of unitized shipments must be evaluated, particularly with respect to the space needed in the receiving area. Unitized shipments require relatively large receiving areas, because rail cars and trucks are unloaded faster than merchandise can be moved from the receiving area to the storage and selection areas. Space must therefore be provided for the temporary storage of full pallet loads until they can be moved.

Adequate space should also be provided in the receiving area for the palletizing of merchandise that is received unpalletized and for the inspection of merchandise that comes into the center.

3. *Average store order.* Stores remote from the distribution center generally receive fewer but larger deliveries than do stores relatively near the center. Stores whose rent per square foot is high generally devote a minimum of space to storage areas and a maximum of space to the sales area. They therefore tend to receive smaller but more frequent deliveries.

The size of the average store order is an important factor in determining whether the center layout will provide for the selection of an entire store order by a single order picker or by several order pickers. It also helps to determine how much space will be required for repack operations. Smaller orders for less-than-case-lots are generally filled from the repack room.

The number of deliveries and distances traveled are also important factors in planning the layout of the food distribution center. Short hauls and frequent deliveries increase the requirements for dock space, in comparison with long hauls and less frequent deliveries. To expedite shipping operations, nearby space must be available for use as a staging area in which to assemble and check orders that have been selected for stores before they are loaded onto trucks.

4. *Mixed loads.* It is important to know whether loads of dry groceries being shipped to the stores will be mixed with other merchandise and, if so, to what extent. If mixed loads will be shipped consistently, the layout of the dry groceries area must be so made that dry groceries ready to be loaded can be merged conveniently with non-foods, produce, meats, or other categories of merchandise that will be shipped together with the dry groceries.

5. *Timing of deliveries.* If stores are equipped for night receiving, the loading of trucks can be timed so as not to interfere with the unloading of incoming merchandise, and the same dock space can be used for both purposes at different times. If outgoing merchandise must be loaded during the day while incoming goods are being received, more dock space is required.

6. *Other factors.* The systems of ordering merchandise from suppliers, store ordering, service-level control, and distribution center merchandise turnover control affect the amount of merchandise handled in the center at any given time and, consequently, affect the layout.

Basic layout principles

Once the flow plan has been established, the planner can lay out the interior space of the building in a manner that will assure the most efficient movement and storage of merchandise. For maximum efficiency, the interior space must be planned before the final shape of the building is determined.

Although the over-all plan of the interior space depends on the flow plan for a particular center, the details of the layout are determined by certain principles, which are considered basic to operating efficiency:

1. The fastest moving merchandise should be closest to the loading dock.

2. Merchandise should be moved the fewest possible number of times.

3. Merchandise should be moved the shortest possible distance. Heavy items, especially, should be stored near the receiving and shipping docks. High-cube, bulky cases that are difficult to handle should also be stored near the loading areas.

4. Receiving and shipping should not be carried on at the same dock at the same time, to minimize confusion and loss of merchandise. However, the same dock space may be used at different times for receiving and shipping, depending upon the demand; this procedure minimizes the backup of merchandise awaiting movement into or out of the distribution center.

5. Column spacings should be so planned that the resulting bays in the building will accommodate the maximum number of pallets. Wasted space between columns should be kept at a minimum.

6. Clear ceiling height should be planned to accommodate the desired number of pallet loads of merchandise. Generally, space is allotted for pallets stacked five high in storage areas.

7. Access to switches, valves, thermostats, and other controls should be so planned that merchandise will not have to be moved and little space will be lost.

8. Valuable goods and merchandise to be shipped in less-than-full-case lots should be handled in a secure room or area separated from the remainder of the working area.

9. Areas that do not require high ceilings, such as rooms for mechanical equipment, rest rooms, and office space for supervisors, should be so located that it becomes practicable to place above such areas mezzanine space for office purposes.

10. The need for additional space should be anticipated in the original layout.

Applying the principles

In a specific distribution center, one or two of these principles may be considered less important than others for the sake of achieving maximum over-all efficiency. For example, to achieve a smooth flow of selection and shipping, it is desirable to compress the greatest practicable number of facings of merchandise into the selection area. When this is done, extensive backup stocks cannot be stored in the selection area. If backup stocks are stored elsewhere, they must be moved into the selection area as they are needed. Thus, they will be handled twice—once to place them in reserve storage and once to place them in the selection line—before they can be selected to fill store orders.

Ideally, full pallet loads would have been moved directly from the receiving dock to the selection area to avoid multiple handling and hand stacking in smaller-than-pallet-load quantities. The layout planner must decide, however, which system will yield the greatest efficiency in the day-by-day operation of the warehouse.

The planner's goal

The system on which the distribution center layout is based should take into consideration an additional principle that governs the total operation. It is: *The planner's goal is to maintain the lowest possible cost of doing business for the entire company while maintaining the highest possible level of service to the stores.*

Some warehouse technicians tend to think only of economies in the operation of the food distribution center. If these economies are achieved at the expense of the stores served by the center, and if the net total effect on the entire operation is that the stores sustain costs greater than the savings at the distribution center, then the warehouse economies achieved are false.

For example, it is possible for a distribution center to maintain minimum inventories by shifting a large part of the storage function to the stores. Stores would then have to invest considerable amounts of money in unnecessarily high inventories. This would result in a decrease in the funds available for other purposes, such as modernization or expansion. Furthermore, the cost of occupancy is much lower for a distribution center than for a store. Hence, the total operation would sustain higher costs, although the distribution center itself would appear to be run at lower cost.

Planners today, in fact, recognize the interrelationship of the distribution center and the stores by devising methods of reducing store inventory and reducing store backroom space. They are interested in reducing the total cost of doing business. Thus, the layout of a food distribution center is planned with that goal in mind.

Once a layout has been planned, however, only trial and error can determine its worth. In the end, whatever plan is devised will be subject to change as operating experience indicates how it may be improved.

6 MATERIALS HANDLING EQUIPMENT

A food distribution center is essentially a facility where large quantities of relatively heavy merchandise are moved in a scheduled, repetitive fashion. Mechanical equipment of various kinds is well adapted to this sort of operation.

The fact that large quantities of merchandise are moved makes it economically feasible to invest in equipment to do the work. The fact that the movement of merchandise is scheduled and repetitive means that equipment is used throughout the day and not sporadically, thereby further justifying the necessary investment. Finally, the fact that merchandise is relatively heavy means that machine power, rather than man power, may be used effectively to do the lifting and hauling of the loads.

The proper selection of equipment involves choosing machinery that is best adapted to the system of operation that has been devised for the distribution center. The equipment used for each operation is selected on the basis of (1) its efficiency in performing its assigned task, and (2) its compatibility with the equipment used for all the related operations in the distribution center.

The selection of equipment is affected, for example, by the frequency of merchandise movement. One system may call for the bulk of incoming merchandise to be placed directly in the selection line. In this case, a number of high-capacity fork-lift trucks may be specified to move large loads directly to the selection line. Another system may call for the bulk of incoming merchandise to be placed in storage initially and later moved to the selection line. In addition to the high-capacity fork-lift trucks that would be required to place the incoming goods in the storage area, a number of lower capacity fork-lift trucks would probably be needed to move smaller loads from the storage area to the selection line as the merchandise is needed.

The selection of equipment is also affected by the kinds of loads (weight and bulk) that will be handled. For example, bulky, lightweight loads, such as paper products, may be too large and cumbersome to be placed on conveyors. They can, however, be handled efficiently by clamp-lift trucks which, in effect, grab the bulky, lightweight loads between two arms and lift them. On the other hand, conveyors would be specified for the efficient handling of small, uniform-sized cartons of merchandise, such as frozen foods.

To insure maximum use of a piece of equipment, work should be found for it throughout each day. If the equipment is to be used throughout the day for a limited number of operations, special-purpose equipment should be specified. An example of special-purpose equipment is a conveyor line that runs between two fixed points and is engineered to carry items of predetermined dimensions. If the equipment is to be used throughout the day for a variety of operations, versatile equipment should be specified. An example of versatile equipment is an industrial truck with a number of attachments which permit the equipment to handle loads with or without pallets or to raise the operator to where he may pick merchandise to a height of 20 feet.

The selection of equipment is further affected by the design of the distribution center. Some of the design and construction factors to be analyzed before equipment is selected include the following:

1. *Dimensions of the warehouse.* Both horizontal and vertical distances are important in determining the equipment that will be selected for a specific warehouse, since they affect where merchandise will be placed, how high it will be stacked, and the routes along which it will be moved. The widths of aisles, the dimensions of doors, the heights of over-the-road trailer doors and rail car doors, as well as the amount of interior space available for maneuvering, are obviously factors that also affect the specifications for equipment to be used in a distribution center.

2. *Character of the floor.* The flooring material used in the warehouse, as well as the floor load capacity per square foot, affects the type of equipment specified. For example, the weight of loaded lift trucks would be related to the ability of the floor to support them. Modern food distribution centers are usually planned so that the floors are capable of sustaining the maximum weight that is likely to be placed on them. Although every effort is made to maintain a level grade, occasionally an addition to an existing warehouse may be higher or lower than the original structure, and the ability of equipment to handle loads going upgrade should be considered.

3. *Cleanliness and ventilation requirements.* A food distribution center is an enclosed space in which food is handled. Fumes, grease, and oil may be injurious to both personnel and merchandise. The need for cleanliness and proper ventilation is therefore a major consideration in the selection of mechanical equipment.

Investment and maintenance costs

When decisions are made on the selection of specific equipment, the following cost factors are considered:

1. *Initial investment.* Most heavy equipment used in distribution centers is amortized over a 10 year period; that is, the cost of the equipment is spread over 10 years and, theoretically, a fund is built up so that the equipment may be replaced at the end of its useful life. To determine whether the investment is justified, initial investment, calculated on the basis of annual amortized cost, is always related to the amount of work the equipment is expected to do.

2. *Anticipated life of equipment.* Some equipment is useful long after its theoretical useful life is over. Other things being equal, if one piece of equipment is expected to be used efficiently for 15 years and another for only 10 years, the former would be specified.

3. *Cost of accessory equipment and facilities.* Attachments for industrial trucks, such as fork extensions and push-pull devices, which add to the versatility of equipment, are available. The operation of certain equipment, such as battery-powered fork-lift trucks, is dependent upon the availability of accessory equipment, such as spare batteries and battery chargers. The cost of accessory equipment, as well as of the space needed to accommodate it, must be considered.

4. *Cost of fuel or power.* In food distribution centers the two major sources of power for mobile equipment are electric batteries and L-P gas-driven motors. The relative costs of these power sources are considered as a factor in equipment selection.

5. *Maintenance and repair.* All mechanical equipment must be properly maintained if it is to operate at high efficiency. Distribution

center managers maintain records of maintenance and repair costs of various types of equipment and consult these records as an aid in specifying new equipment. If equipment can be serviced by a company's own personnel on its own premises, operating costs are likely to be lower than if outside service personnel must be called in or if the equipment must be moved to an outside servicing facility. The most important cost factor in this connection is related to the time required for servicing. Equipment that can be serviced by available personnel with available facilities is likely to be ready for more hours of useful work than equipment that must await the convenience of outside personnel.

Basic materials handling equipment

The basic types of equipment used in food distribution centers include the following:

1. *Fork-lift trucks.* These basic tools in food distribution centers can withdraw, lift, carry, position, and place large amounts of merchandise. The tines of a fork-lift truck are slipped under a pallet, and the load supported by the pallet is lifted, transported, lowered, or deposited—all under the control of an operator.

Exhibit 4. Types of Materials Handling Equipment

Electric walkie pallet truck (top, left); counter balanced fork-lift truck (bottom, left); and reach-type fork-lift truck (right).

Fork-lift trucks are designed to handle loads up to 4,000-5,000 pounds and pallet sizes up to 48 inches by 48 inches. They elevate loads as high as 210 inches above floor level and can travel at speeds of five to seven miles an hour.

Fork-lift trucks may be classified broadly as counterbalanced and straddle types. The counterbalanced fork-lift truck is heavier than the straddle type and has a wider turning radius. Counterbalanced equipment requires an aisle 9-to-12 feet wide for right-angle stacking, while the straddle type can operate in an aisle 6-to-8 feet wide, since it has a shorter length than the counterbalanced machine. The straddle type, however, can handle only wing-type pallets so designed that the fork-lift truck's wheels can be positioned under the load to provide stability. The weight of the counterbalanced machine is in the rear. The machine can carry a load, on any type of pallet, on forks extended in front of it; the weight of the load is counterbalanced by the weight of the rear of the truck. The mast can be tilted forward 5 degrees and backward 10 degrees.

A variation of the straddle type is a reach-type fork-lift truck which will operate with a flush-type pallet; it has a short wheel base and a scissor-type extender fork.

Various attachments for lift trucks are available for performing specialized functions.

2. *Pallet jacks.* This equipment lifts a pallet load of merchandise about four inches and, in effect, places wheels under the load. Pallet jacks may be operated manually or electrically. Electrically powered jacks may be of either the walkie or the rider type. The pallet jack supplements the work done by the fork-lift truck; it moves merchandise short distances.

3. *Pallets.* A pallet is essentially a platform on which merchandise is stacked. The purpose of a pallet is to permit a large quantity of items to be handled as a single unit. The wooden pallet provides a base for handling merchandise with fork-lift trucks and pallet jacks.

Pallets are usually made of hardwood held together with cement-coated screw-type nails. The standard sizes of pallets used in food distribution centers are 48 inches by 40 inches and 32 inches by 40 inches. Since the depth, 40 inches, is the same for both sizes, the pallets can be used interchangeably. A dry groceries warehouse is usually built with 40 feet of clear space between columns, so that the maximum number of pallets may be placed in each clear space.

An industry wide survey of food chain companies by the National Association of Food Chains has brought full endorsement of the concept of pallet standardization, with preference indicated for the 48″ × 40″ four-way hardwood pallet, and with the 32″ × 40″ four-

Exhibit 5. Types of Pallets

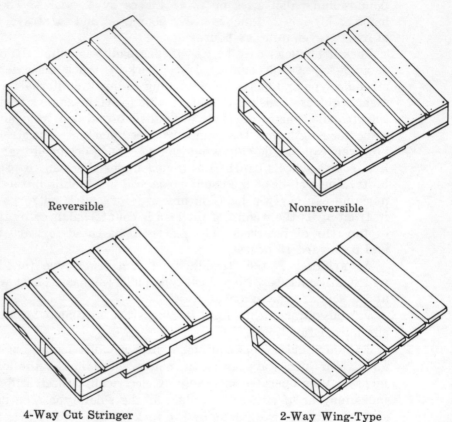

Reversible

Nonreversible

4-Way Cut Stringer

2-Way Wing-Type

way hardwood pallet as an alternative. The 48″ × 40″ pallet has been adopted by the Grocery Manufacturers of America and by the military. It fits into both rail cars and trucks.

Pallets fall into these classifications: reversible or nonreversible; two-way or four-way entry; and wing type or flush type.

A reversible pallet has enough cross members so that merchandise may be stacked on either side. A nonreversible pallet has cross members close together at the top for stacking goods and has a wider space between cross members at the bottom so that the wheels of the pallet jack may enter.

Two-way entry means that a fork lift or pallet jack may engage the pallet only from the ends, and four-way entry means that the pallet may be entered from the ends and the sides.

A wing-type pallet has cross members extending over the edges of the stringers (horizontal members connecting the uprights) at the top and is designed for two-way entry with either a fork lift (usually the straddle type) or a pallet jack. A flush-type pallet has cross members that end flush with the outside edge of the stringers. It may have either two-way or four-way entry and is usually used with counterbalanced and reach-type fork-lift trucks.

4. *Pallet racks*. When one pallet load of merchandise is placed directly on top of another pallet load, the merchandise on the lower pallet is not accessible until the upper pallet load is removed. To overcome this problem, merchandise on pallets is placed on racks

Exhibit 6. Pallet Racks

which act as a divider between vertically stacked pallet loads. Pallet racks are usually constructed of steel sections that provide support for pallet loads placed in the rack, converting each pallet, in effect, into a shelf. The steel sections can be dismantled, thus making it easy to move the racks and set them up elsewhere in the warehouse if the floor layout is changed.

5. *Order-selector trucks*. Merchandise picked for a store order is placed on pallets that are carried on the beds of selector trucks. These trucks are usually four-wheelers whose sizes are determined by the width of the selection aisle; four-wheelers must pass one another as

Exhibit 7. Order Selector Train

well as fork-lift trucks in the aisle. The four-wheeler may be pushed or pulled manually by the order selector, or it may be pulled by a tractor, or pulled by an endless chain called a towline.

Where a towline that runs around the perimeter of the selection area is in operation, the selector trucks are fitted with devices permitting them to be attached to the line so that they may be towed automatically to the staging area. In some cases, devices attached to the trucks may be set so that the trucks will be automatically shunted off the towline at predetermined points. A pin on the truck may be set to engage any one of nine or ten switchpoints.

Order-selector trucks may also be hooked up into "trains" of two or more four-wheelers, attached to a tractor. The tractor may be driven by the order selector or controlled by radio or by electrical impulses passing through a tape on the floor.

6. *Towlines.* A towline is an endless chain. Four-wheelers are hooked up to the towline and transported in a fixed pattern. The towline may be moving below the level of the floor or suspended from the ceiling. The overhead towline is more flexible than the underfloor towline, because the path of the overhead towline may be changed at less expense. The in-floor towline, however, places less wear on the connections between four-wheelers and the chain than does the overhead towline, although breaks in the in-floor chain usually take more time to repair. An overhead towline may also limit the load heights and mast heights of fork-lift trucks passing under it.

Exhibit 8. In-floor Towline

Exhibit 9. Overhead Towline

A variation of the towline is a guide wire which is taped to or buried in the floor or strung overhead. An electrically controlled tractor follows the guide wire without any physical connection and moves without an operator. Radio waves that control the tractor are sent from signal boxes installed throughout the warehouse or at either end of the route. A tractor is summoned to a station by pushing a button. If the guide wire is not buried in a concrete floor, the route may be changed easily.

7. *Conveyors.* These are machines on whose surfaces merchandise is directly placed and transported. Three basic types of conveyors are used in food distribution centers: roller, wheel, and endless belt. The roller and the wheel types use the force of gravity. The endless belt is electrically powered and is used where merchandise must be conveyed up an incline. The various types of conveyors may be used in combination with one another.

8. *Additional equipment.* Many other types of materials handling equipment are used in food distribution centers. They include:

- Clamp attachments for industrial trucks. The clamps are like a giant pair of pliers. They exert pressure on the load from the sides, thus holding the load firmly as the truck moves.
- Slip sheets of cardboard that serve the same basic function as pallets.
- A variety of containers and attachments for mobile equipment, such as pushers and front racks for counterbalanced fork-lift trucks.
- Containers that are lifted by jets of air between the load and the floor, permitting loads to be pushed easily by hand.
- Hand trucks.
- Electric scooters and carts for supervisory personnel.
- Gravity shelving and flow racks. These are slanted fixtures on which merchandise slides down to replace merchandise that is taken from the front.
- Elevators in multifloor warehouses.
- Electric dumbwaiters.
- Automatic dock levelers that are adjusted to connect the truck bed to the loading dock and that provide a bridge between the truck and the dock.

The future

Food distribution centers in recent years have consistently increased their use of mechanized methods. Distribution executives are constantly investigating new equipment that holds the promise of reducing costs and increasing productivity. Hand in hand with the adoption of new equipment, however, must go the devising of new systems. It is in the area of systems of operation that distribution executives look for major advances in the next few decades, with the development of new equipment following the directions indicated by the new methods of operation.

MATERIALS HANDLING SYSTEMS

Order selection is the central function of the distribution center. The planner must develop a method of operation that will provide for a smooth flow of merchandise within the selection area, as well as to and from that area.

Most of the merchandise in a distribution center is stored in the selection area. Order pickers draw on it as they select store orders. A reserve storage area is used for additional inventory and for bulky merchandise that cannot conveniently be placed in the selection area. It is generally open space so located that it feeds conveniently into the selection area.

An important supplementary area is the repack room, which serves as both a storage area and a selection area for valuable goods and for items ordered by stores in less-than-case lots.

Because all merchandise feeds into or out of the selection area, the planner generally devises a system of operation for that part of the center first.

Selection methods

The basic methods used in the selection of dry groceries are:

1. *Part of each store order is filled in a designated small area.* This method of selection calls for the large dry groceries selection area to be split into a number of smaller areas. Each order selector receives store order-picking sheets that list only the items stored in the selection area for which he is responsible. Thus, each order selector picks only part of a store's order. The mix of items in each area should result in all selectors having relatively even work loads. Ideally, each aisle would contain merchandise with the same average sales frequency and weight.

The selection of items ordered by one store takes place at about the same time in each of the smaller selection areas. Selected merchandise is then brought to a staging area near the shipping dock, and the store's entire order is assembled there before being loaded on a truck. This method of operation requires relatively short selection lines clustered around a staging area.

Each smaller selection area is so laid out that, ideally, the order selector can go through an assigned pattern of movement, starting from one point in the selection area with an empty vehicle and arriving at the staging area with a full load of merchandise. If a high percentage of vehicles arrive at the staging area fully loaded, the system is making efficient use of manpower.

When the order selector has delivered a load to the staging area, he returns to the selection area and proceeds to fill part of the order of a second store.

2. *The entire store order is picked from a large selection area.* The second major method of selection calls for each order selector to fill an entire store order from a single large dry groceries selection area. The order selector goes through an assigned pattern of movement from one point in the large selection area, filling vehicles with merchandise as he moves through the aisles.

This method of selection usually requires an automatic means of moving vehicles filled with merchandise from the selection area to the staging area. As a filled vehicle is automatically moved away from the selector, he begins filling an empty vehicle with additional merchandise. When he has completed one circuit of the selection line, he has filled an entire store order. He then obtains picking sheets that list a second store's entire order and proceeds to fill it in the same way.

3. *Variations of the basic methods.* To obtain maximum efficiency, distribution centers occasionally combine the two basic methods. For example, an unusually large order from one store may be divided among two or more order selectors working within one large selection

area. As another example, an order selector working within a smaller selection area may find that the next store's order is not ready to be filled, and he may proceed to another smaller selection area in order to help complete the selection of another store order.

Selection equipment

The basic selection system used affects the type of equipment specified. Because manpower costs are the largest single operating expense, the planner provides as much equipment as possible to help reduce the amount of direct labor required. As one distribution executive puts it, "Equipment is never absent or temperamental and draws no fringe benefits."

With the exception of systems in which selected merchandise is placed directly on a conveyor, some form of wheeled merchandise carrier is provided on which the order selector places the merchandise he takes from the selection area to fill store orders. For most distribution centers, the basic equipment used in the selection process is a four-wheeled merchandise carrier.

The order selector moves through the selection area in a prescribed pattern, accompanied by a wheeled vehicle on which he loads a store order as he selects the required items. He may place the selected items on the bed of the vehicle or, more commonly, on a pallet previously placed on the bed of the vehicle.

If part of each store order is filled in a designated selection area, the order selector generally pushes or drives the loaded merchandise carriers directly to the staging area where a store's order is assembled for shipment.

If the entire store order is picked from a large selection area, a method must be devised to transport the merchandise from the selection area to the staging area. The following methods are commonly used:

1. *The towline method.* A towline moves in a fixed pattern from the selection area to the staging area. When an order selector has loaded a four-wheeler with merchandise, he hooks the loaded carrier to the towline and the carrier is automatically moved to the staging area.

After a carrier is unloaded at the staging area, it is hooked to the towline and is automatically moved back to the selection area, providing a supply of empty carriers to be used by order selectors in picking additional orders.

The towline usually runs around the perimeter of the dry groceries warehouse. An order selector loads a carrier in the selection area and moves the loaded carrier to the perimeter, where he hooks it to the towline and obtains an empty carrier. In very large installations, two or more towlines may be in operation, each running around one designated area of the distribution center.

In some installations, the towline runs through the selection area itself instead of on the perimeter. In such cases, the towline passes directly in front of all the merchandise that is to be selected.

The order selector unhooks a four-wheeler from the towline, makes a number of selections, and then rehooks the four-wheeler so that the towline does the work of pulling the load to the next point at which he is to make a number of selections. If only one or two cases have to be selected from a number of facings of merchandise, the order selector may not unhook the four-wheeler from the towline; the towline moves slowly enough to permit an order selector to place a few cases on the four-wheeler while it is in motion.

The order selector continues the process until he has selected a full load and then permits the four-wheeler to continue on its way to the staging area while he unhooks an empty four-wheeler from the towline and continues to select merchandise for the store whose order he is filling.

When a selection aisle has a towline, the aisle must be wide enough to permit both selection traffic and towline traffic. Usually, the space is wide enough for selection traffic on both sides of the towline. Some planners consider this to be a costly use of space.

Use of the towline method permits selection lines to be placed at some distances from the staging area, as transportation of fully loaded four-wheelers from the selection area to the staging area is fully automatic. During the hours the distribution center is in operation, the towlines do not stop moving unless there is a mechanical breakdown.

2. *The "train" of four-wheelers.* If a towline is not installed, some other method of moving heavily loaded four-wheelers through the selection area and on to the staging area must be devised. One major method is the use of tractors to pull "trains" of two or more four-wheelers.

The order selector moves the "train" through the selection area, picks the merchandise needed to fill a store order, and transports the "train" of loaded carriers to the staging area. At the staging area, he picks up a "train" of empty carriers and returns to the selection area, where he continues to fill an order either for the same store or for another store.

3. *The conveyor method.* A method of order selection which does not use four-wheelers at all involves the use of conveyors that run through the entire selection area, passing in front of all the merchandise that is to be selected.

One large installation has four conveyor lines fed by four workers, each selecting one-fourth of a store order in a single simultaneous tour of the selection area. As merchandise reaches the end of the conveyor lines, it is loaded into a truck by another four-man crew. The selectors and the loaders exchange functions periodically, a practice that distributes the work load evenly among the men and provides each man with experience in all phases of the operation. The movement of the conveyor lines may be controlled from a station where the entire operation is supervised.

A disadvantage in using conveyors along a selection line lies in the fact that an average order is made up of about 20 percent of the items, according to distribution center engineers. Thus, the order selector spends 80 percent of his time passing unneeded items at the slow walking pace designed for order selection.

Some successful operations that are fully conveyorized along the selection line report that the over-all benefits of a highly visible, easily controlled operation outweigh that disadvantage. Most food distribution centers, however, use conveyors for specialized applications; for example, to move filled containers from a repack room to a staging area or to move merchandise automatically through a slicing, weighing, and prepackaging operation.

Each selection method has its proponents. Most planners will agree, however, that the best technique can be determined only after complete analysis of the circumstances under which the operations are to be performed.

The "filing system"

The mechanical operation of the selection system is one major factor the planner must consider. A second is the method of placing the merchandise so that it may be easily found by the selector. The planner must devise, in effect, a "filing system" for the merchandise.

The "filing systems" used in the dry groceries sections of distribution centers are based on a unit of space called a "slot." A slot is a designated position on the floor of the warehouse, usually the width of one pallet. A slot may be deep enough to accommodate from one to seven pallets on the floor.

A slot is usually identified by a number so placed that it may be easily read by the selector. Numbers follow an ascending sequence on the selection line. One system calls for odd numbers on one side of an aisle and even numbers on the other side. Another system calls for numbers in ascending sequence to run up one side of an aisle and to continue down the other side.

The two basic "filing systems" for dry groceries are the fixed-slot system and the variable-slot system.

1. *The fixed-slot system.* Under the fixed-slot system, a number is assigned to each item of merchandise, and the item is placed in the slot bearing that number, in quantities sufficient to fill store orders. When the merchandise is received, a receiving clerk refers to a code book that contains the numbers designating the locations of all items. As he receives merchandise, he marks each pallet load to indicate the slot to which it should be taken.

The term "fixed slot" may be misleading, in a sense, because the slot locations of individual items may change from time to time. For example, if canned pumpkin is normally inventoried in a quantity of less than 100 cases, its normal slot location would be in an area where the slots are one pallet deep. As Thanksgiving approaches, however, canned pumpkin inventory may increase to 600 or 700 cases, and a new slot location—perhaps six pallets deep—would be designated for the item. The receiving clerk would mark the receiving document with the new slot number and the data processing department would take note of that new number. This procedure reduces the need to place items in a separate reserve storage area and to handle them twice.

In general, however, the fixed-slot system requires a "home" location for each item. Merchandise may be placed in slots where it is easiest to handle. Items belonging to the same commodity group do not have to be placed together. Because all modern distribution centers are run with the aid of either computers or tabulating equipment, it is relatively easy to convert orders as they come from stores into order-picking sheets, on which items are listed in the sequence in which they are located on the warehouse floor. Hence, the need to place related commodities together so that they can be identified by a selector has largely disappeared.

There are, however, general guidelines for the sequence in which merchandise is placed in the selection area under the fixed-slot system. For example, the fastest-moving items are generally placed toward the end of the selection line so that they are moved the shortest possible distance to the staging area. A study of an operation in which order selectors push hand trucks indicated that merchandise placed in the selection line without regard to sales velocity required 59 percent more distance to travel for assembly of an order than was the case when merchandise was placed in the selection line in accordance with sales velocity.[1]

In addition to being placed toward the end of the selection line, merchandise that moves in large quantities must obviously be placed in floor slots where pallets can be stored more than one or two deep.

The location of merchandise is also affected by handling require-

[1] U.S. Department of Agriculture, *Marketing Research Report No. 348*, July 1959.

ments. The order selector "builds" a pallet load on the four-wheeler as he selects merchandise. When the full load reaches the staging area, it is removed by a fork-lift truck and must, therefore, be stable. To make it easy for an order selector to build a stable pallet load, items are placed in a sequence that enables selection of compact, regularly shaped merchandise first, providing a base on which to build a pallet load that will not topple.

Some slot locations are left open to accommodate new items, seasonal items, or promotional items. Open slots are usually scattered along the selection line so that items may be placed where they will be easiest to handle. Odd-shaped items that are stacked to "top off" a pallet load are placed with other odd-shaped items.

2. *The variable-slot system.* Under the variable-slot system, merchandise is placed in the first available open slot when it is received. This system tends to avoid double handling of goods. For its successful operation, however, it is completely dependent on accurate, timely reports on the precise location of all items. These reports, fed to a computer, permit the computer to tell the order selector where to look for each item.

A single item of merchandise may be located in one, two, three, or more slots. The computer will list on a picking order the location of the slot containing older merchandise, and only after that slot is empty will it list the slot with more recently received merchandise.

The major advantage of the variable-slot system is that it makes maximum use of available space. No calculations are required to determine how much space must be allocated to each item in the selection area—a procedure that must be followed in the fixed-slot system. However, the random placement of merchandise under the variable-slot system limits the amount of control exercised to place items where they are most easily handled.

Both the fixed-slot and the variable-slot systems are combined to a greater or lesser degree in most large warehouse operations. For example, items stored in bulk, such as cereals and soap, are usually placed in a fairly large general area without strict adherence to a fixed-slot system, even in distribution centers that are otherwise run along fixed-slot lines.

Placement of pallets

Dry groceries are stored in the selection area on pallets placed in floor slots or on pallets placed on pallet racks.

1. *Pallets placed in floor slots.* When pallet loads are placed directly on the floor, additional pallet loads may be stacked on top of them. Merchandise placed on the floor, directly on the selection aisle, is

stacked a maximum of two pallet loads high to enable selectors to reach and remove cases from top pallets.

Immediately behind the pallets that are directly on the aisle are additional pallet loads of the same merchandise. They constitute a "working reserve" stock. These may be stacked as much as five high. Some distribution directors, however, make it a practice to limit all stacks in the selection area to two high so that fork-lift operators need not continually bring high-stacked pallet loads down to working levels. "Space is cheaper than manpower," they point out in explanation of this policy.

2. *Pallets placed on pallet racks.* If pallet racks are used, the slots are only one pallet deep as this is the limit of the reach of the fork-lift truck. The racks would have to be dismantled for the truck to gain access to any back-up merchandise.

Pallet racks are used in a selection line for items that, because of their small size or slow movement, do not require more than two or three pallets for maximum storage. They increase the number of selection fronts on the assembly line by giving the selector ready access to items on each of the two or three vertical sections on which the pallet loads are placed. Selection is usually made from the lower sections, with the upper section used to hold reserve stock.

90°- versus 45°-angle stacking

There is some controversy concerning the angle at which pallets should be placed on the selection aisle. Some planners favor 90° slots, while others favor 45° slots. Proponents of either view have a plausible case.

The major advantage claimed for 90°-angle stacking is that this method allows for more merchandise facings on a selection line and

Exhibit 10. Space Required with 90° and 45° Angle Storage

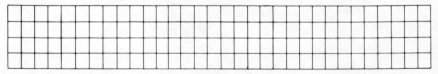

45° angle storage: 44 facings; 110 pallets on the floor

90° angle storage: 64 facings; 128 pallets on the floor

Exhibit 11. 45° Stacking

Exhibit 12. 90° Stacking

therefore permits quicker selection of items with less walking than is the case with 45°-angle stacking. In addition, when pallets are placed at right angles to the aisle, slot depths are uniform and the entire floor area (other than aisle space) may be occupied by merchandise.

The major disadvantage of 90°-angle stacking is that it requires wider aisles than does 45°-angle stacking, since a fork-lift truck requires more room for maneuvering to handle merchandise stacked at right angles to an aisle. Right-angle slots require fork lifts to make full turns to service the slots, unless special equipment that can operate in narrow aisles is used.

The major advantage claimed for 45°-angle stacking is that the total operation—including servicing the slots as well as selecting from them—is more efficient.

The disadvantage of stacking pallets at a 45° angle is that floor space is unused to some extent.

The factors of space available for the merchandise itself and space required for aisles probably cancel each other out so far as the relative space advantages of each method are concerned. The planner usually gives consideration to both methods of stacking and selects the one that in his opinion works best in terms of the efficiency of a specific distribution center's entire operation.

Similarly, no single system of selection may be characterized as "best." In each case, the system must be evaluated in terms of how well it serves the over-all purpose of a specific distribution center.

RECEIVING
AT THE DISTRIBUTION CENTER

Merchandise shipped to a distribution center must be moved through the receiving area on schedule and with reasonable speed. Otherwise the flow of operations through the entire center will be slowed down.

Inbound merchandise should be unloaded as soon as possible after it arrives at the distribution center. However, when too many trucks arrive at about the same time, the receiving facilities of the center are strained and the result is that some trucks must wait while others are being unloaded.

It is costly for loaded trucks to stand by idly. The drivers must be paid for time spent waiting to unload. Moreover, the owner of the equipment is deprived of its use; a few hours' delay may make it impossible for a truck to return to a supplier for a second load in time to deliver it the same day.

Scheduling truck arrivals

With careful scheduling, many companies have been successful in spreading the receiving load at the distribution center and, thus, minimizing waiting time.

Suppliers are notified when their shipments are expected to arrive and, in some cases, scheduled arrival times are placed on purchase orders. In many cases, local suppliers are requested to deliver at about 6 A.M. so that receiving docks may be cleared for the delivery of out-of-town loads whose arrival time is less predictable.

When a truck arrives at the distribution center, its time of arrival is recorded and, if it is on time, the next available dock space is assigned to it. At some distribution centers, truckers receive numbered cards to indicate when their turns will come to unload, together with estimates of waiting time.

Some food distribution centers have established express receiving lines for loads of 150 or fewer cases. Thus, small deliveries may be handled expeditiously without interrupting the flow of large deliveries through the receiving area.

Unloading delays

Once a truck has backed up to the receiving dock, the speed with which it is unloaded depends to a large extent upon the efficiency and skill of the driver. However, speed without accuracy is self defeating. At the receiving dock, every piece called for in a shipping document must be checked to insure that it has been delivered and received in good condition. If the load consists of several kinds of merchandise that have not been separated by brands and sizes, the driver is obliged to separate the items on the receiving dock so that the receiving clerk may check the delivery against the shipping document. The way in which merchandise has been loaded on the truck is obviously an important factor in the receiving operation.

Thus, unscheduled truck arrivals, inefficient unloading, and careless loading may contribute to delays, and some trucks may be detained at the distribution center beyond the times considered standard for the amounts of merchandise they have delivered.

Uniform Motor Detention Rule

A controversial regulation recently prescribed by the Interstate Commerce Commission penalizes food distribution centers, among others, that do not release trucks in a "reasonable" amount of time after they have arrived to make deliveries. The regulation is called the Uniform Motor Detention Rule.

Under its provisions, all motor carriers must collect detention penalties if their trucks are not released within the periods specified in the regulation for various types of loads. Those detention penalties vary with the section of the country in which a shipment originates, and they are based on wage rates in the area of origin.

The controversy surrounding the Uniform Motor Detention Rule stems from the fact that the amount of time a truck is delayed may seldom be controlled strictly by the receiver of merchandise. As noted, trucks that arrive at unscheduled times and are unloaded too slowly by drivers cause the major delays.

To avoid delays, most retail food companies are placing stricter controls on scheduling. In the opinion of food retailing executives, scheduling of inbound trucks is becoming a must for the food industry. One distribution executive says, "The trucker cannot be allowed to continue to come knocking on our doors and expect to be serviced on the spot."

Detention charges add unnecessarily to the cost of distribution, since solutions are available to the problem of delays in the unloading of trucks. Careful time checks are being made of arrivals, unloading, and departures at many food distribution centers, and meetings are being held regularly with the operating managements of truck lines to call attention to poor situations. As with many practical problems, however, no single solution seems to work for every company affected. In the long run, the answer will undoubtedly lie in improved communications between the trucking companies and the distribution centers.

The impact of unloading delays is not as sharp in the case of rail cars as it is in the case of trucks. Railroads allow some free time for unloading. Furthermore, rail cars are unloaded by warehouse personnel who are under the direct control of the food distribution center's management.

Unitized shipments

The most important recent development in the reduction of costs in the receiving operation is the introduction of the unitized shipment on an increasingly widespread scale. This method of shipment calls for from 30 to 100 cases of merchandise to be placed on a wooden pallet or on a corrugated or fiberboard slip sheet so that the entire quantity may be handled as a unit by use of a fork-lift truck, pallet jack, clamp lift, or other transporter.

The manufacturer ships merchandise on wooden pallets (costing about $3.50 to $4.50 each) or on corrugated slip sheets (costing about 13 cents to 25 cents each) or on fiberboard slip sheets (costing about 50 cents each). The wooden pallets are reused many times, while the slip sheets are used once and then discarded. Since the goods in a unitized shipment are already on pallets or slip sheets, no manual labor is required to palletize them in the receiving area.

More receiving space required

As indicated in Chapter 5, one result of increased unitization is the need for increased space in the receiving areas of food distribution centers.

Hand-stacked merchandise taken out of trucks and placed on pallets can be pulled away from the receiving dock as soon as it is palletized. Two fork-lift operators moving loaded pallets from the receiving dock to storage areas can keep pace with the unloading of seven trucks.

Unitized loads, however, are pulled out of trucks so fast that five fork-lift operators would be needed to keep pace with the unloading of seven trucks.

To keep man power and equipment costs low, palletized incoming merchandise is kept on the receiving dock until it can be taken away without increasing the number of men and fork-lift trucks used for that purpose. Therefore, to accommodate the accumulated pallet loads of merchandise awaiting transfer to storage, the receiving area has to be increased in size.

Loading and unloading costs

The cost of loading and unloading a rail car or truck is reduced sharply when merchandise is unitized, in comparison with dead piling —the manual stacking of cases on the floors of rail cars or trucks.

When wooden pallets are used, however, a loss of about 10 to 15 percent in the capacity of the vehicle is suffered. Mathematically, a 30 percent loss in capacity is suffered. However, the total capacity of a truck or rail car is seldom used. Consequently, the practical experience of many companies indicates that only a 10 to 15 percent loss is suffered. This disadvantage is overcome by the fact that the speed of loading and unloading results in significant reductions in turn-around time. Equipment is tied up for shorter periods during loading and unloading; hence, equipment is used more efficiently.

Studies of unitization made so far do not provide final answers on exact savings, but they do point up the fact that substantial savings are possible.

For example, a study of 700 shipments by rail of more than 1,000,000 pieces weighing almost 35,000,000 pounds indicated that the labor cost of unloading unitized shipments was $9 per rail car compared with $20.89 per rail car for hand-stacked, floor-loaded shipments.[1]

The study also revealed that one food distribution center saved $10,000 in labor costs in one year when unitized loads were received from 14 rail cars per week compared with none the previous year.

[1] *The Unit Load Explosion*, a report prepared by Better Management Services, Staten Island, N.Y., September 1966, for the U.S. Department of Agriculture.

Loading rail cars

According to a study made under the direction of Dr. Earl H. Brown, Professor of Business Management at Cornell University, the wooden pallet method had the highest average labor productivity with respect to man-hours per car, cases per man-hour, and units per man-hour for the loading of grocery products on rail cars, as Tables 3—6 indicate.[2] The slip sheet method, however, achieved more tons per man-hour than the wooden pallet method in loading rail cars. The average weight per case and the average weight per handling unit were considerably higher for the products loaded on slip sheets, so that, according to the report, the comparison may not be entirely valid.

Loading trucks

In the loading of trucks, the study dealt almost exclusively with the

[2] *An Analysis of Grocery Shipments from Grocery Manufacturers to Food Chain Warehouses*, by Byron Oliver, Thomas McThenia, and Earl H. Brown, Cornell University, 1965.

Table 3
MAN-HOURS PER CAR REQUIRED TO LOAD GROCERY PRODUCTS
ON RAIL CARS BY HANDLING METHOD
85 Rail Cars, 1965

Handling Method	Number of Cars	Man-Hours Per Car	
		Average	Range
Dead Pile	19	7.4	3.3 - 10.7
Slip Sheet	12	3.4	1.2 - 7.8
Wood Pallet	25	3.0	1.3 - 6.0
Mixed Clamp Lift*	1	4.7.	—
Mixed Slip Sheet*	28	5.6	1.7 - 9.9

*Dead Pile in Doorway

Table 4
TONS PER MAN-HOUR ACHIEVED IN LOADING GROCERY PRODUCTS
ON RAIL CARS BY HANDLING METHOD
85 Rail Cars, 1965

Handling Method	Number of Cars	Tons Per Man-Hour	
		Average	Range
Dead Pile	19	3.8	2.2 - 8.8
Slip Sheet	12	10.1	4.4 - 26.6
Wood Pallet	25	6.9	3.1 - 11.8
Mixed Clamp Lift*	1	8.3	—
Mixed Slip Sheet*	28	5.2	2.1 - 15.0

*Dead Pile in Doorway

Table 5

CASES PER MAN-HOUR ACHIEVED IN LOADING GROCERY PRODUCTS
ON RAIL CARS BY HANDLING METHOD

85 Rail Cars, 1965

Handling Method	Number of Cars	Cases Per Man-Hour	
		Average	Range
Dead Pile	19	306	142 - 634
Slip Sheet	12	623	356 - 1348
Wood Pallet	25	787	251 - 1960
Mixed Clamp Lift*	1	531	—
Mixed Slip Sheet*	28	443	249 - 1199

*Dead Pile in Doorway

Table 6

UNITS PER MAN-HOUR ACHIEVED IN LOADING GROCERY PRODUCTS
ON RAIL CARS BY HANDLING METHOD

37 Rail Cars, 1965

Handling Method	Number of Cars	Units Per Man-Hour	
		Average	Range
Slip Sheet	12	8.7	4.1 - 20.3
Wood Pallet	25	16.2	5.3 - 28.0

Table 7

MAN-HOURS PER TRUCK REQUIRED TO LOAD GROCERY PRODUCTS
ON TRUCKS BY HANDLING METHOD

51 Trucks, 1965

Handling Method	Number of Trucks	Man-Hours Per Truck	
		Average	Range
Dead Pile	27	3.7	1.1 - 5.5
Clamp Lift	1	1.4	—
Wood Pallet	23	1.8	.7 - 3.8

wooden pallet and dead pile methods. No trucks in the study were loaded by the slip sheet method and only one was loaded by clamp lift. According to all four measures of productivity, the wooden pallet method was superior to the dead pile method. (Tables 7—10.)

Table 8
TONS PER MAN-HOUR ACHIEVED IN LOADING GROCERY PRODUCTS
ON TRUCKS BY HANDLING METHOD
51 Trucks, 1965

Handling Method	Number of Trucks	Tons Per Man-Hour	
		Average	Range
Dead Pile	27	4.3	1.5 - 8.3
Clamp Lift	1	15.3	—
Wood Pallet	23	8.6	2.8 - 32.1

Table 9
CASES PER MAN-HOUR ACHIEVED IN LOADING GROCERY PRODUCTS
ON TRUCKS BY HANDLING METHOD
51 Trucks, 1965

Handling Method	Number of Trucks	Cases Per Man-Hour	
		Average	Range
Dead Pile	27	268	33 - 445
Clamp Lift	1	1126	—
Wood Pallet	23	636	379 - 1251

Table 10
UNITS PER MAN-HOUR ACHIEVED IN LOADING GROCERY PRODUCTS
ON TRUCKS BY HANDLING METHOD
24 Trucks, 1965

Handling Method	Number of Trucks	Units Per Man-Hour	
		Average	Range
Clamp Lift	1	21.1	—
Wood Pallet	23	13.0	8.5 - 24.6

Unitized receiving

From the foregoing, it is apparent that unitized shipping is advantageous to manufacturers in the transportation of merchandise from their plants to food distribution centers.

What are its advantages (and disadvantages) from the point of view of the receiving department of the food distribution center?

In general, it costs less to unload unitized shipments than it does to unload goods shipped by the dead pile method. Mechanical equipment can handle unitized loads far more efficiently than manual labor can handle individual cases.

At the present time, however, one important question concerning truck receipts has not been fully resolved. Traditionally, the unloading of trucks was performed by the drivers making the deliveries to the distribution centers. With the advent of unitized shipping and the need for mechanical equipment to perform the unloading function, warehouse personnel has had to take on the unloading function, thus adding to the cost of receiving.

As manufacturers, retailers, and wholesalers acquire more experience with unitized receiving, adjustments will undoubtedly be made to allocate cost equitably. During that adjustment period, however, some differences of opinion on the feasibility of unitized truck shipments may be expected between shippers and receivers. A major food chain executive comments: "The trucker stands to gain the most and we feel he will have to 'give' a little to make this system a success."

Unloading rail cars

Merchandise received by rail has traditionally been unloaded by the receiver. Consequently, the case for unitized receiving by rail is clearly unquestioned.

For rail receiving, the Cornell study indicates, the average labor productivity was highest for the wooden pallet method on the basis of all four measures of productivity. Whether measured in terms of average man-hours per car required to unload grocery products, average tons per man-hour, average cases per man-hour, or number of units per man-hour, the wooden pallet method was clearly superior to

Table 11

MAN-HOURS PER CAR REQUIRED TO UNLOAD GROCERY PRODUCTS
FROM RAIL CARS BY HANDLING METHOD

121 Rail Cars, 1965

Handling Method	Number of Cars	Man-Hours Per Car	
		Average	Range
Dead Pile	73	6.5	2.2 - 16.3
Slip Sheet	10	2.4	1.1 - 5.2
Wood Pallet	14	1.1	.7 - 3.1
Mixed Slip Sheet*	22	5.7	2.2 - 10.1
Mixed Wood Pallet*	2	2.2	1.4 - 2.3

*Dead Pile in doorway

Table 12

TONS PER MAN-HOUR ACHIEVED IN UNLOADING GROCERY
PRODUCTS FROM RAIL CARS BY HANDLING METHOD

121 Rail Cars, 1965

Handling Method	Number of Cars	Tons Per Man-Hour	
		Average	Range
Dead Pile	73	3.8	1.4 - 8.6
Slip Sheet	10	14.6	7.4 - 27.6
Wood Pallet	14	23.8	6.4 - 55.8
Mixed Slip Sheet*	22	4.9	1.1 - 17.3
Mixed Wood Pallet*	2	11.9	10.5 - 15.1

*Dead Pile in doorway

Table 13

CASES PER MAN-HOUR ACHIEVED IN UNLOADING GROCERY
PRODUCTS FROM RAIL CARS BY HANDLING METHOD

121 Rail Cars, 1965

Handling Method	Number of Cars	Cases Per Man-Hour	
		Average	Range
Dead Pile	73	299	81 - 478
Slip Sheet	10	701	381 - 1022
Wood Pallet	14	1759	453 - 3877
Mixed Slip Sheet*	22	352	166 - 972
Mixed Wood Pallet*	2	701	549 - 1021

*Dead Pile in doorway

Table 14

UNITS PER MAN-HOUR ACHIEVED IN UNLOADING GROCERY
PRODUCTS FROM RAIL CARS BY HANDLING METHOD

121 Rail Cars, 1965

Handling Method	Number of Cars	Units Per Man-Hour	
		Average	Range
Dead Pile*	73	7.3	3.4 - 15.6
Slip Sheet	10	11.8	6.3 - 23.1
Wood Pallet	14	37.6	17.0 - 70.7
Mixed Slip Sheet**	22	5.7	4.4 - 10.2
Mixed Wood Pallet**	2	14.7	14.1 - 15.3

*Cases were stacked on wood pallet units during the unloading operation.
**Dead Pile in doorway.

the slip sheet method, the dead pile method, or methods combining dead pile in the doorway with either slip sheets or wooden pallets. The superiority of unitized receiving of rail shipments was clearly demonstrated. (Tables 11—14.)

Unloading trucks

Merchandise received by truck was unloaded with greatest efficiency when fork-lift trucks were used to move pallet loads from the vehicles to the receiving docks. Wooden pallets handled by fork-lift trucks required the fewest man-hours to unload vehicles, with the clamp lift

Table 15

MAN-HOURS PER TRUCK REQUIRED TO UNLOAD GROCERY PRODUCTS
FROM TRUCKS BY HANDLING METHOD

314 Trucks, 1965

Handling Method	Number of Trucks	Man-Hours Per Truck*	
		Average	Range
Dead Pile	204	2.5	.1 - 7.5
Wood Pallet-Hand Jack	18	.7	.1 - 3.7
Wood Pallet-Electric Jack	59	.8	.5 - 2.3
Wood Pallet-Fork Lift	6	.4	.3 - .8
Clamp Lift	11	.5	.2 - 2.5
Mixed Wood Pallet**	16	2.9	.3 - 5.5

*Includes partial loads
**Partial Dead Pile

Table 16

TONS PER MAN-HOUR ACHIEVED IN UNLOADING GROCERY
PRODUCTS FROM TRUCKS BY HANDLING METHOD

314 Trucks, 1965

Handling Method	Number of Trucks	Tons Per Man-Hour	
		Average	Range
Dead Pile	204	3.6	.3 - 11.9
Wood Pallet-Hand Jack	18	11.9	2.0 - 25.0
Wood Pallet-Electric Jack	59	16.0	2.0 - 48.0
Wood Pallet-Fork Lift	6	37.5	12.0 - 67.2
Clamp Lift	11	28.2	10.0 - 63.0
Mixed Wood Pallet*	16	4.4	.9 - 16.9

*Partial Dead Pile

Table 17

CASES PER MAN-HOUR ACHIEVED IN UNLOADING GROCERY
PRODUCTS FROM TRUCKS BY HANDLING METHOD

314 Trucks, 1965

Handling Method	Number of Trucks	Cases Per Man-Hour	
		Average	Range
Dead Pile	204	300	51 - 878
Wood Pallet-Hand Jack	18	713	405 - 2317
Wood Pallet-Electric Jack	59	1259	273 - 4166
Wood Pallet-Fork Lift	6	3600	1514 - 4213
Clamp Lift	11	1642	702 - 3600
Mixed Wood Pallet*	16	331	54 - 2413

*Partial Dead Pile

Table 18

UNITS PER MAN-HOUR ACHIEVED IN UNLOADING GROCERY
PRODUCTS FROM TRUCKS BY HANDLING METHOD

83 Trucks, 1965

Handling Method	Number of Trucks	Units Per Man-Hour	
		Average	Range
Wood Pallet-Hand Jack	18	14.6	3.6 - 19.9
Wood Pallet-Electric Jack	59	19.0	4.4 - 74.7
Wood Pallet-Fork Lift	6	50.5	30.1 - 66.5

method a close second. The same pattern was noted with respect to tons per man-hour and cases per man-hour. On the whole, the use of electric jacks with palletized loads was more efficient than the use of hand jacks. (Tables 15—18.)

The dead pile method

In the transportation of grocery products from both suppliers to distribution centers and from distribution centers to stores, the dead pile method of shipping still predominates. However, since unitized handling methods are used in virtually all internal operations, both in suppliers' plants and in distribution centers, it is not unreasonable to predict that unitized shipping, both to and from distribution centers, will predominate in the future.

From the viewpoint of the manufacturer, the dead pile method is advantageous, because it is flexible, permits maximum use of rail car and truck capacity, permits the use of standard rail cars and all sizes of trucks, lends itself to less-than-truck-load shipments, and requires the least amount of equipment.

However, major disadvantages cited by manufacturers in the Cornell study are that the dead pile method requires the greatest amount of labor and makes it difficult to control damage, pilferage, and errors.

From the viewpoint of the food distribution center, the dead pile method has these advantages: it permits small-order quantities, requires the least amount of equipment, and provides the best opportunity to detect damaged merchandise.

On the other hand, the dead pile method requires the greatest amount of labor for handling inbound shipments and results in the poorest utilization of dock space.

The wooden pallet method

From the manufacturer's point of view, the wooden pallet method of shipping has these advantages: it is the method preferred by purchasers of large quantities of merchandise, achieves high labor productivity, is suitable for all types and mixtures of products and for both rail and truck shipments, costs less per use than slip sheets (which are discarded after a single use), does not reduce fork-lift capacity, requires low maintenance and equipment cost, does not require additional dunnage (packing to prevent cargo shifting), and provides good visibility for fork-lift operators.

The disadvantages cited by the manufacturers are: pallets must be returned, exchanged, and repaired; their use requires specially equipped rail cars, specifically assigned for palletized shipments; they reduce the capacity of rail cars and trucks; additional warehouse space is required to store unused pallets; merchandise damage in transit is greater than with slip sheets or with merchandise stacked for clamp-lift handling.

At the distribution center, the major advantages of receiving on wooden pallets are: it is most compatible with existing internal handling systems, results in high labor productivity, does not reduce fork-lift capacity, permits fork-lift operation in aisles narrower than 12 feet, permits a load to be lifted from any of its four sides, provides good visibility for fork-lift operators, and permits handling with relatively inexpensive hand jacks and electric jacks.

Disadvantages cited by the distribution center are that pallets have to be returned or exchanged and that pallet sizes must be uniform for maximum efficiency.

The slip sheet method

The main reason some manufacturers prefer the slip sheet method is that slip sheets are disposable and need not be returned, exchanged, or repaired. They do not require special rail cars and are suitable for all types and sizes of products. They do not reduce the capacity of rail cars as much as do wooden pallets and, it is claimed, their use results in less damage in transit than does the use of wooden pallets, which bump up against each other, causing damage.

The disadvantages cited by manufacturers are: the cost of slip sheets is higher per use than the cost of wooden pallets, slip sheets require additional equipment cost and maintenance, and their use reduces the visibility of fork-lift operators and the capacity of fork-lift trucks. Moreover, when merchandise is double-decked, the upper deck must be separated from the lower to permit entry of fork-lift tines. Because loads on slip sheets are less secure than they are on wooden pallets, damage in loading is greater than with wooden pallets. In addition, the use of slip sheets requires a highly skilled operator, who may not always be available.

On the receiving end, distribution centers prefer slip sheets because their use results in higher labor productivity than does dead piling. The problem of handling and returning empty pallets is eliminated, and merchandise on slip sheets can be placed as a unit on various sizes of wooden pallets. One major food chain comments: "We have had some good experience with slip sheets on trucks, particularly with canned citrus and frozen citrus, and baby food. If your trailer is hooked up to a tractor and the forks of your unloading vehicle are long enough, there is no reason the slip sheet cannot be used."

Distribution centers cite these disadvantages of slip sheets: reduced labor productivity, compared with the wooden pallet method; reduced fork-lift capacity; reduced visibility and maneuverability which cause product damage; the need for wider aisles, and additional equipment and maintenance cost.

The clamp lift method

The clamp lift method has these advantages for manufacturers: eliminates most of the problems associated with the use of wooden pallets and slip sheets; results in higher labor productivity than dead pile; does not require assigned rail cars; is suitable for both rail and truck shipments and for various sizes of unit loads; permits faster handling as well as the handling and shipment of partial units or single layers of merchandise; and facilitates the removal of damaged cases in the unit.

On the negative side, the clamp lift method is not suitable for all types of products, reduces rail car capacity, requires additional equipment and maintenance costs, reduces the capacity of equipment, and reduces the visibility of equipment operators. Furthermore, the use of this method slows stacking at heights and there is a danger of stacks collapsing because exposed sides of stacked cartons absorb moisture.

At the distribution center, the use of clamp lifts is reported by one food chain to eliminate the need for pallets, the cost of repairing pallets, and the internal handling of pallets by fork-lift operators and selectors.[3] Stack capacity is increased by the ability of the clamp load operator to stack odd numbers of layers in a stack and the elimination of the space required for the wooden pallet. Moreover, space is not needed for pallet storage. In addition, a clamp truck allows one to handle a flexible size unit load, with the ability to adjust for narrow or wide loads so that an entire area may be used for storage. Damage is reduced, compared with situations in which the block of merchandise does not exactly fit a wooden pallet, so that overhanging (merchandise hanging over the side of a pallet) causes crushing while underhanging (merchandise not fully covering the pallet) causes toppling.

Clamp handling, however, is not conducive to the piling of dissimilar items on top of one another. On the other hand, when pallets are used, dissimilar items may be readily stacked and handled easily. In addition, the clamp must be used with a device that shifts the load from side to side, resulting in a more expensive piece of equipment than a conventional fork-lift truck. The extra equipment needed increases the total weight of the truck by about 1,000 pounds. Since the combined weight of the truck, the extra equipment, and the load is limited by the ability of the motor to move it, the heavier clamp-lift truck hauls about 1,000 pounds less than a comparable fork-lift truck.

On balance, clamp lifts are looked upon with favor in the handling of high-cube, low-density, high-velocity items such as paper products. One company now handles with clamps 125 selected items that it previously handled on pallets, and finds that less handling time is required, since the items do not have to be placed on pallets and can be quickly piled so that the clamp lift can grasp them.

An overview of unitized loads

Whichever method is adopted as most suitable to a class of merchandise—whether the wooden pallet, the slip sheet, or the clamp method—the thrust of unitized shipping will be felt increasingly in the receiving departments of food distribution centers because of the substantial savings that are possible.

The extent of the savings will depend on: (1) the type of merchandise shipped; (2) the specific method used—whether with slip

[3] Stop & Shop, Inc., Boston.

sheets, wooden pallets, containers or loads that can be moved by clamp lifts; (3) the efficiency with which a rail car or a truck is loaded to provide stable, easily handled loads; (4) the type of equipment used in shipping; and (5) the type of equipment used in unloading.

Although the advantages of unitized shipping and receiving far outweigh the disadvantages, difficulties are being experienced with some unitized loads. According to a recent report,[4] improper handling and stowing and incompatibility of the dimensions of packages and pallets lead to problems such as these:

1. Merchandise may be placed on a pallet incorrectly so that a load falls apart as it is picked up by a fork-lift truck at its destination. A correct pallet pattern calls for cases to be placed so that they support one another and provide a stable load.

2. If merchandise hangs over the sides of a pallet, owing to incompatibility in the dimensions of the containers and the pallet, crushing may result. If a pallet is not fully covered by merchandise, the load may shift in transit, leading to damage and difficulty in handling at the destination.

3. Merchandise may be stacked on double-decked pallets which cannot always be handled easily at the destination.

4. Pallets may be stacked too high to be handled by fork-lift trucks, requiring manual labor to unload items at the tops of the loads.

5. Mixed cases on a single pallet may have to be taken off the pallet by hand and segregated, then restacked before being taken to storage.

6. Bulkhead doors may not be latched properly, so merchandise is not well supported during transit and arrives in damaged condition.

7. The equipment that a distribution center has available for unloading unitized shipments may not be the right equipment. For example, some unitized shipments are being unloaded with heavy-duty fork-lift trucks costing from $8,000 to $10,000 each, when the task can be done with electric pallet jacks at $2,000 to $3,000 each.

Obviously, much trial and error work will be done with unitized loads before maximum efficiency is achieved.

Coding the merchandise

Whether inbound merchandise is handled by the dead pile method of shipping or as a unitized load, each item is checked for accuracy by the receiving clerk as it is placed on the receiving dock. In most dry groceries operations, the receiving clerk then consults a book which contains the code number of each item. The code number, which

[4] *The Unit Load Explosion,* Better Management Services.

indicates where the item should be placed in the storage-selection areas, is marked on one case in each pallet load and the pallet load is then hauled to its floor location by a fork-lift truck or a pallet transporter. If the quantity to be received of an item is unusually high—generally for seasonal or special-purpose merchandise—the receiving clerk may change the location code number and assign a new location for the item.

The receiving clerk also enters the location code number on the receiving document. He then sends that document to the data processing department where the location code number and the product code number are entered in the data processing system, together with the quantity received.

Through the data processing system, an up-to-the-minute inventory is maintained on all items that move through the distribution center.

DATA PROCESSING AND THE DISTRIBUTION CENTER

The maintenance of accurate and timely records is essential to the complex process of moving a large number of items of merchandise in and out of a food distribution center.

Most of the records relate to the status of individual items of merchandise. The recording system shows whether an individual item has been ordered, is in transit to the distribution center, is in storage, or has been selected and shipped to a store. It also shows where each item is stored within the distribution center, how much it cost, how much it weighs, how it is packed, and when it was received.

Analysis of the records permits management to determine whether inventory levels at the distribution center are in balance with the demands of the stores.

The entire process of balancing distribution center inventory against store demand, at the minimum investment in merchandise consistent with supplying a steady flow of desired items to the stores, is called inventory management.

The recording and analysis of the information required to manage inventory is called data processing. The three key elements in the operation of any data processing system are (1) input, (2) processing of data, and (3) output. When a computer is used, the process is called electronic data processing, or EDP.

In food distribution centers, inventory management is the principal use to which computers are put. One of the major purposes of sound inventory management is to minimize the investment in inventory. Information available through electronic data processing permits a distribution center to maintain a high rate of inventory turnover which, in turn, minimizes the investment in inventory.

For example, if in the course of a year a distribution center supplies stores with dry groceries whose total cost value is $45,000,000, and if its rate of turnover is 15 times a year, then the average inventory is worth $3,000,000 ($45,000,000 ÷ 15). A turnover of 15 times at the distribution center is not uncommon for dry groceries.

If, however, a way were to be found to increase the distribution center's turnover to 20 times a year, then it could supply stores with $45,000,000 worth of merchandise at cost, while maintaining an average inventory of only $2,250,000 ($45,000,000 ÷ 20).

Increasing turnover from 15 times to 20 times would have the effect of reducing inventory at cost by $750,000, freeing that amount of money for expansion or other investments.

Careful analysis and application of information made available through EDP permits merchandising executives at the distribution center to increase turnover.

Too high a rate of turnover, however, can result in "outs" at the warehouse so that many items ordered by stores would not be available. Too high a rate of turnover can also result in many small shipments being made to the distribution center instead of fewer large shipments, thus leading to an inefficient receiving operation.

Inventory management seeks, therefore, to fill store demand with the maximum number of items ordered while increasing turnover to the highest rate consistent with efficient operation. Electronic data processing is an important tool used by distribution center operating and merchandising executives to achieve these purposes.

The computer

Electronic data processing is a very fast way of adding and subtracting. Rapid addition and subtraction, in turn, are equivalent to rapid multiplication and division. Multiplication is performed by successive addition, and division by successive subtraction. Thus, EDP is a very fast way of adding, subtracting, multiplying and dividing numbers.

A computer is a machine that performs these arithmetical operations. However, it performs one additional function that makes it more than a counting machine. It "remembers" large amounts of information and it produces that information on demand.

Other machines, in common use, perform the same functions as does the computer. The adding machine found in every office, for example, "remembers" a long list of numbers and, on demand, produces a total. The adding machine also subtracts. An electric adding machine can add numbers rapidly enough so that it may be used to multiply them, and it can subtract numbers fast enough so that it may be used to divide them. Although it does not multiply and divide efficiently, it can, nevertheless, perform these calculations.

Historically, the adding machine is an ancestor of the electronic computer. The basic difference between the two is that the computer performs the operations of addition, subtraction, multiplication, and division at blinding speed and is capable of remembering vast quantities of numbers. Hence, it may be used to process an enormous amount of information or data. It does so at such high speeds that it can produce answers to many problems that could not heretofore be solved on a practical level because of the vast amounts of time needed for computation.

Electromechanical tabulating equipment—the immediate predecessor of the electronic computer—does some of the same things that a computer does. However, its "memory," or data and program storage, is in the form of punched cards rather than in the equipment itself, and it processes information at a much lower rate of speed.

The sophisticated computers and related equipment that have been developed by scientists, mathematicians, and engineers for functions requiring high-speed data processing are extremely difficult for the layman to understand. Nevertheless, a basic understanding of what a computer is and what it can do is not difficult to achieve.

In the field of food distribution, relatively few people need to know in detail how a computer operates and exactly how to give it the instructions it needs to perform its work. As the business of distributing food becomes more complex, however, more and more people will have to learn, at least in general terms, what a computer and related equipment can do.

Today, executives in company administration, distribution center operation, transportation, finance, control and accounting, personnel, merchandising and buying, sales promotion, market research, and store locations analysis must know enough about computers to be able to understand the reports they generate and to suggest problems they might be called upon to solve.

In the near future, many stores will be linked with central computers. Store operators will have to know what information to send to the computer, how to send it, how to understand the answers that come back from the computer, and what to do about those answers.

Just as we are able to drive an automobile without having to understand every detail of its construction and operation, so will we be able to use computers at store level. By following simple, routine directions, store personnel will be able to give the computer the information it requires and to understand the information the computer sends back.

Input

A computer is neither a thinking machine nor a giant brain. It can work only with the information given to it. There are various ways in which data is put into a computer, but all have one common factor: they use coded input. That is, the information fed into a computer, such as a store order, is in the form of numbers that may represent either words or numbers.

The basic language of a computer consists of two numbers—1 and 0, which are known as binary numbers. All information fed into the computer is in the form of the numbers 1 and 0, combined in such a way as to make up any numbers desired, or to stand for any word or group of words.

For example, the number of cases of a brand and a size of canned tomatoes received in a shipment from a vendor, or the items and quantities ordered by a store, is "input." In coded form, 3456 may represent "Brand A, Canned Tomatoes, in No. 2½ cans," and 10 may represent "10 cases." The coded input would then be the number 3456 followed by the number 10, which would be read and translated automatically into the basic computer language of 1 and 0.

Computers can read input data that has been keypunched into conventional punched cards, recorded on magnetic tape or wire, punched into paper tape, or printed, typed, or in some cases handwritten.

There are many methods of feeding input to a computer, such as:

1. *Punched cards.* Holes are made in a conventional punched card through a process called keypunching. The holes are placed in various positions corresponding to numbers that can be read by a computer. The conventional punched card can also be read by electromechanical tabulating equipment.

2. *Mark-sense cards.* Marks are placed with a graphite pencil in various positions on a mark-sense card. The position of each mark corresponds to a number. A mark-sense card cannot be read directly by a computer, but a conventional punched card can be created from a mark-sense card by a machine that reads the mark-sense card and punches the corresponding holes in a punched card. Many supermarkets now order from distribution centers on mark-sense cards.

3. *Magnetic tape.* The holes in punched cards or the marks on mark-sense cards (which have been first converted into punched cards) are converted into signals on a magnetic tape or wire (similar to the tape or wire used in home recorders). The signals may then be recognized at high speed by a computer.

A more recently developed device, similar to a keypunch, puts the information directly onto magnetic tape instead of punched cards. Magnetic tape can be fed directly into the computer at a considerable saving of time over punched card input.

4. *Magnetic discs.* The data from punched cards or mark-sense cards is converted to a magnetic disc, from which, in turn, signals are fed into the computer.

5. *Punched paper tape.* Information may be punched into paper tape as a by-product of another function. A punched paper tape recorder (similar again to a home tape recorder) may be wired to a business machine such as a cash register, adding machine, accounting machine, or time clock. Any information recorded on the parent machine is punched into paper tape that can later be fed into a computer.

6. *Optical character recognition.* Adding machines print stylized characters on a tape that can be read "optically" by a computer and can be also read by the human eye. The adding machine tape is prepared in the store as a store order and is sent to the warehouse, where it is fed into the computer. This process replaces the keypunching or mark-sense converting operation at the warehouse. Several hundred stores may order through one warehouse, using one adding machine in each store.

In the near future, optical character recognition may capture the item movement of many grocery products by having the checker index the item code number on the cash register during the checkout process. The resulting tape would be sent to the data processing center where accurate reports on item movement would be furnished by a computer.

7. *Optical document reading.* An entire original document is shown to a computer and read "optically." This method is not yet perfected to the point where all kinds of printing and handwriting on various sizes and shapes of documents may be read under conditions that apply to the practical operation of food distribution centers. In the near future, however, optical document reading will undoubtedly play a major role in speeding up the input process. All the information, or selected parts of it, contained in an entire page would be read optically. The use of optical systems, either optical character reading or document reading, permits the use of a single, original entry. The manual operations of keypunching or mark-sense marking are bypassed, thus saving considerable time and effort and insuring faithful input of data on the original document into the computer storage.

8. *Telephone and teletype transmission.* Any data that can be punched into paper tape or recorded on magnetic tape or wire may also be transmitted over ordinary telephone lines. Thus, through the use of equipment operated somewhat like an adding machine, an entire store order may be placed on magnetic tape or punched paper tape at the store. The data on the tape may be translated into signals that can be transmitted automatically over the telephone through a special device. The data may be fed directly into a computer or translated back to punched paper tape, magnetic tape, or cards and fed into a computer later on.

An order may be entered on to paper tape or magnetic tape at a very low rate (about 30 to 45 minutes per grocery order) and transmitted by telephone at a much higher speed to the central computer office. The speed for transmission would be about 3 to 10 minutes.

When the tape is read into a computer, at a much higher speed, as little as 5 seconds would be needed for the entire grocery order to be entered into the computer.

Transmission may take place at times when telephone lines are least busy and, hence, cost less to use. Transmission may be begun automatically on a signal from the food distribution center at its convenience or on a predetermined schedule, so that the sending and receiving equipment need not be attended.

Another communication system that may be used with computers involves the use of teletypewriters that produce and receive both printed copies and punched paper tape in two-way transmission, permitting an 800-item order to be sent in 10 minutes or less.

A related system uses a 10-key adding machine. The order is entered on the adding machine at the store and recorded on a magnetic tape cartridge at the same time that it is printed out on the adding machine tape. When the complete order is entered, the signals on the magnetic tape are sent over the telephone to the distribution center, where another magnetic tape picks up the signals. With this system, a 1,000-item order may be sent in less than three minutes.

These procedures for supplying input to computers from remote points, or variations of them, are now in use by some food companies. As food retailers are able to justify its economic feasibility, data transmission from supermarket to distribution center, as well as from distribution center to supplier, may be expected to increase.

It is estimated that eight out of 10 food distributors in the United States who are already using computers will have networks for the transmission of data by 1970 or will be actively examining ways to acquire networks.[1]

---

[1] "The Role of Electronic Computers in Chain Store Management," *Report of the 9th Technical Symposium of the CIES*, Philadelphia, November 1965, p. 80.

One of the major problems facing the users of computers today is that the time required to prepare information in a form in which it can be read by a computer is great in comparison with the time required for a computer to read and process the data. Hence, great efforts are being made to speed up the total input process.

The methods described above give information to a computer. The next problem is: What does the computer do with the information and how does it do it?

Processing of data

To tell a computer what to do and how to do it, a process called "programming" is employed. A trained technician must learn what problems are to be solved and must obtain a crystal-clear definition of each problem.

Every step of every calculation that will be required to produce an answer to a problem must be worked out in advance by a person trained to do so. The programmer, in effect, tells the computer how to work on the information that will be fed to it, and the computer will perform each operation in exactly the same way whenever a specific type of problem is presented to it.

The computer does what a programmer has told it to do under specific sets of circumstances. It performs its work, as noted, by adding and subtracting very rapidly.

We have seen, for example, that when a new shipment of canned tomatoes arrives, the computer is told that fact through the use of a code number applying only to that brand and size of canned tomato, and it is also told the quantity of cases in the shipment.

Responding to instructions previously given to it by the programmer, the computer adds the received quantity to the inventory on hand. It has been programmed to do so.

Similarly, when the item is withdrawn from the distribution center to fill a store order, the quantity withdrawn is subtracted from the quantity on hand to provide a new record of the quantity remaining in inventory.

When physical inventories are taken periodically in the dry groceries warehouses of food distribution centers, a variation of only a very small fraction of 1 percent is usually found between the value of the inventory as determined by the computer and by the actual physical count. Picking errors—primarily failure to select all the items ordered—account for most of the discrepancies, so physical count usually shows more inventory than the "book value" determined by the computer. Pilferage, where it occurs, would of course reduce inventory.

An original program for a computer involves a great many individual instructions, each of which must be given to the computer in a precise sequence of numbers. Methods of programming are available, however, whereby common English words are used instead of numbers and these words are automatically translated into entire sequences of numbered commands to the computer.

Because the computer is capable of seeking and finding the quantities associated with many things, when properly programmed it can produce information about *relationships* that, in a practical sense, is available through no other means.

For example, the computer can list the quantities received and withdrawn of item No. 3456 for a three-month period in the current year, for the corresponding three-month period in the preceding year, for the immediately preceding three-month period in the current year, and for the corresponding three-month period in the preceding year. It stores information fed into it and computed by it, and it produces that information on demand when programmed to do so. This procedure, in general terms, is called "the processing of data." The computers and associated equipment are called "hardware" and the program packages that tell them what to do are called "software."

Output

The information produced by a computer is printed out so that it may be read and understood by anyone who can read English. The binary numbers with which the computer works are translated automatically into decimal numbers that are familiar to everyone. The code numbers referring to things are, when necessary, translated into words in the English language, for example, Brand A, Canned Tomatoes, No. 2½ can.

The invoices that accompany store orders are examples of computer printouts. They identify the items and the quantities shipped and indicate, in each case, the cost and/or retail value. They also show the total weight of the order.

If desired, an invoice can show the total cubage of an order. Such information helps the transportation department to decide how to load trucks most efficiently.

The output that computers are capable of producing is expected to affect markedly the methods of operation not only of food distribution centers, but of supermarkets as well. For many companies, some computer applications discussed below are already realities. For many more, these procedures will in the near future help to shape their programs in merchandise management, food distribution center operation, and supermarket operation.

While not every food distribution center has its own computer, the time is rapidly approaching when virtually every food distribution center will find economic justification for maintaining a computer on the premises.

In some cases, distribution centers use the services of outside organizations whose computers fill the needs of a number of companies. It is normally not practicable, however, to use outside service computers for daily functions such as order processing, because output must be available in a steady flow. An outside service organization, handling the work of many companies, cannot always provide an uninterrupted flow of output for a single customer.

Output of interest to stores

The output of most immediate interest to the stores consists of store order forms, warehouse order picking forms, store invoices, and "scratch" lists.

1. *Store order forms.* Store order sheets or books are printed routinely by computers as by-products of inventory control systems. Each item is generally listed by name in the proper sequence within a merchandise family grouping. This procedure permits store orders to be written in an orderly fashion, since most stores are laid out with merchandise arranged in family groups.

The store order forms also list the code number and the shipping unit for each item.

2. *Warehouse order picking forms.* Although the store order forms list items in family groupings for the convenience of store personnel in checking shelf inventory against the order forms, most food distribution centers cannot select merchandise from the original orders as they come from the stores.

The sequence in which items are listed on the store order form seldom corresponds to the sequence in which the merchandise is to be found on the warehouse floor. At the warehouse, it is seldom efficient to place merchandise in the selection line in the same physical sequence in which it may be found in the stores. Factors such as rate of movement, method of handling, bulk, relative quantities, and distribution of work loads of warehouse personnel are considered before a slot is assigned to a commodity. Items belonging to various commodity groups may be placed close to one another for convenience and efficiency in handling. Thus, the store order, as it is received from the store, is virtually useless in guiding an order selector in his work. Therefore, the items on the store order form must be rearranged into a list that follows the same sequence as do the actual items to be selected.

The computer produces such a list. It does so by reshuffling each item into a sequence that has been programmed in advance to correspond to the sequence in which merchandise is placed in warehouse slots.

As the computer produces the warehouse picking list, it scratches out-of-stock items and adds such information as the cost and/or retail price of each item and the total weight of the shipment or of each major portion of the shipment.

Electromechanical tabulating equipment can perform these tasks and still does so for many food companies. The computer, however, performs the work much faster, permitting the processing of a larger number of store orders, and it also produces a great many reports that are beyond the time limitations imposed on tabulating equipment.

3. *Store invoices.* The warehouse picking list, or a copy of it, usually is the document that accompanies the shipment to the store. Sometimes the list of the items ordered is reassembled into the original sequence as listed on the store order and sent to the store as its invoice. In either case, the computer quickly produces the document.

4. *Scratch lists.* An item may have been scratched by the computer because the warehouse was out of that item at the time a store's order was being processed. That situation occurs only rarely.

More frequently, however, an order selector may scratch an item because it was not available in the slot where it was supposed to be, while it may have been in a reserve stock area. On occasion, an order selector may miss an item as he moves down the selection line. At the end of each day, a list of scratched items is compiled. This list may then be compared with a warehouse inventory list, and distribution center executives can readily determine whether order selectors are in fact servicing the stores properly.

The daily warehouse inventory list is produced by the computer. Since the computer is told throughout each day how many cases of a specific item are received and how many cases of that item are shipped out to stores, and since the computer already knows how many cases of that item were on hand at the beginning of the day, obviously it can provide an inventory on that item at the end of each day.

If the above procedure is followed for every item handled by the distribution center, at the end of each day a complete item-by-item inventory list may be produced. This list also represents the next day's beginning inventory.

Daily comparison of the warehouse inventory list with the scratch list is important, because it permits management to take prompt action to remedy the following three unfavorable situations:

(a) Stores are not being serviced properly and will lose sales on out-of-stock items.

(b) Warehouse inventory is not being turned over fast enough.

(c) Store personnel must reorder the scratched items, or the distribution center's computer system must "back order" the items, so that they will be delivered when they next become available. In either case, a good deal of time and money will have been spent unnecessarily.

Output for merchandisers

A number of reports may be produced to assist merchandisers and buyers to decide what to purchase and when to purchase it. These reports have to do with the movement of commodities.

1. *Commodity group report.* Commodity group reports may be produced to show the weekly movement (or daily movement, if desired) out of a distribution center of each of, perhaps, 50 to 100 general classes of merchandise.

These reports show, for each commodity group, total weekly shipments to stores in terms of number of shipping units, dollar costs, retail value, gross profit, and gross profit percentage.

These timely reports may be used by merchandisers and buyers as a guide in evaluating the results of their weekly marketing strategies. Because they deal with large groups of merchandise, these reports indicate only general trends. They also indicate only the rate of movement of merchandise from the distribution center to the stores and not necessarily the actual rate of retail sales. Accurate item-by-item reports of actual retail sales are, however, a possibility, even a probability for the future.

2. *Four-week item report.* Because the computer "remembers" every item shipped to every store and can sort through its memory to provide a total of all shipments of a given commodity, the commodity group report can be further broken down into an item report for any given period of time. The four-week item report gives the total shipments of each item within a four-week accounting period. Thus, every four weeks a merchandiser may see a comprehensive report that lists the total quantities of every item, arranged by family group, that were shipped out of the distribution center.

Since the computer also remembers past sales performance, the sales movement of any item may be traced for the current year and compared with the preceding year. If the trend of sales is up sharply, plans may be made to increase purchases and stores may be alerted to give more display facings to the product on the theory that it pays to push items customers have demonstrated they want.

Since the report also shows gross profit results, it may readily be determined whether increased sales resulted in increased profits. If the sales gains were achieved through sharp price reductions, for example, then the report on sales volume trends tells only part of the story. By a comparison of both sales volume and gross profit, it is possible to judge whether it will be profitable to stimulate additional sales of the item at the gross profit level previously recorded for it.

The key to the use of the merchandise movement report—whether by commodity groups or individual items—is to arrive at a sales goal in terms of the best "mix" of higher-profit and lower-profit items likely to produce the highest sales and the highest total gross profit.

Plans for advertising emphasis of selected items may also be affected by what the report reveals about immediate past performance.

This type of analysis is just as valid and useful for an individual supermarket as it is for a merchandiser at a food distribution center who is charged with making plans for a large group of stores. It is possible for a computer to produce a similar report of merchandise movement for each store it serves, but that is rarely done. In the future, increasing awareness of the possibility of "assortment merchandising" for each store's own specific requirements may lead to increasing use of individual store reports. On the basis of these reports, a supermarket's management may readjust merchandise on the shelves, changing the number of facings of individual items to improve their contributions to sales and gross profit, and eliminating some items whose space yield does not justify keeping them in stock. In any case, an individual store report could be useful in analyzing an unprofitable store, especially if it were to be compared with similar reports from highly profitable stores operating under comparable conditions.

3. *Product movement report by vendor.* A computer can reshuffle the information in its memory units so that it may produce a list of items grouped by vendor. Properly programmed, a computer can forecast the future rate of movement of an item on the basis of the history of its movement, take into account the lead time required to move the item from the vendor's plant to the distribution center (from the time the order is sent), and suggest a quantity that the buyer might wish to order from a specific vendor.

4. *Suggested-order report.* Lists of suggested orders are produced by computers in a number of food companies today. They are intended to be used as guides by buyers rather than as commands to them. A buyer has the opportunity and the obligation to review the suggested orders before he signs and mails them to vendors.

If the warehouse service level of deliveries to stores is satisfactory, some buyers tend to accept the computer's "advice" without further analysis, and merely endorse the computer-generated orders with respect to both timing and quantity. Many other buyers, however, continually probe deeper for opportunities to improve sales and inventory levels and to take advantage of promotional possibilities that may exist in selected stores.

The computer can also round off suggested orders so that the merchandise will be delivered in full pallet quantities. If an item must be ordered in quantities of less than full pallets, the computer can suggest order quantities equivalent to a horizontal level on a pallet, or a multiple thereof, such as 6, 12 or 18 cases as a part of a 36-case pallet.

If the suggested order quantities for a number of items in a single vendor's complete line add up to a total quantity that is large enough, the computer can determine the quantity of each item that should be ordered to make up a complete truck load or carload, conforming to weight restrictions and discount schedules. The computer, then, can remove the guesswork from the tremendous task of making up truck loads and carloads. Again, it should be stressed, the buyer can accept, modify, or reject the computer's suggestions.

As a further by-product of the lists of suggested orders produced by the computer, the machine can develop a purchase order for each vendor. This eliminates the need for typing purchase orders, a costly activity and a potential source of errors.

The computer develops suggested orders through a process of forecasting future requirements. Forecasting systems in inventory management are designed to determine with reasonable accuracy what a company expects to sell of each item. Forecasts can never be exact, but it is possible to adjust each forecast by correcting the errors in preceding forecasts.

A computer is highly reliable in making calculations, but it can work only on the instructions it receives and the data fed into it. Human errors in both programming and input occur at one time or another in the operation of virtually every computer system. Consequently, computer output, especially as it relates to forecasts leading to suggested lines of action, is generally under continual review by the people who must act on the computer's decisions.

In discussing data processing applications to buying, Norman C. Peterson, controller of Ralphs Grocery Company, Los Angeles, stated that "a buyer makes many decisions about every item he purchases." [2] In elaborating on his presentation, Mr. Peterson indicated that there may be as many as 1,000 factors affecting buying decisions. Some of the major factors include current movement, historical movement, seasonal movement, stock on hand, lead time, discounts, allowances, weight, cubage, pallet count, horizontal ties, carload, truck load, com-

[2] "Integrated Data Processing Applications at Ralphs Grocery Company," Norman C. Peterson, *Report of the 9th Technical Symposium of the CIES*, Academy of Food Marketing, Philadelphia, November 1965.

pany advertising, vendor advertising, promotion, service level, space yield, safety stock, merchandise on order, minimum or maximum order quantity, safety factor, review time, and value.

Consequently, a machine-oriented system of inventory management can reduce the detail work that would otherwise be required in buying while permitting a buyer to concentrate on merchandising decisions and items that are exceptions to the rule. As the buyer analyzes a list of suggested orders produced by a computer, he takes into account any unusual situations of which the computer was unaware. Those situations may be brought about by unusual changes in weather, buyers' strikes, fire damage to a store, new Sunday openings or closings, sudden changes in consumer buying preferences due to advertising or publicity (either beneficial or adverse), new store openings that do not adhere to schedules, local catastrophes, price fluctuations, or newly introduced buying arrangements (either favorable or unfavorable).

In the future, it may be possible to program computers so that they will take into consideration all the above factors, as well as many other variables, but at present it is not economically feasible for a food distribution center to install such a complex series of changeable, special-purpose programs.

5. *Excess inventory report.* Reports may be developed by a computer to show the amount of stock on hand that has been in a distribution center more than a specified number of shipping days. If a report is wanted on every item in inventory that is older than 15 shipping days, the information can be produced by a computer and it will be broken down to indicate which buyer is in charge of each group of items. These reports are known as "exception reports" because they contain information limited only to items that behave in an unusual fashion.

A good buyer may be speculating in anticipation of cost increases and may be completely justified in holding inventory in excess of a company's current operating needs. An exception report, however, merely provides an easy way for the head buyer to hold each buyer accountable for his inventory situation. One executive says, "If there isn't some vehicle for holding buyers accountable, it is very likely that the warehouse could become virtually inoperative through product congestion." [3]

6. *Short-supply report.* A report may be produced daily by a computer to show which items are likely to be out of stock within a few days. Such a report would obviously flash a danger signal and, depending on the system used, might precipitate emergency action to

[3] Patrick J. Murphy, Jewel Companies, Inc., Melrose Park, Ill.

make sure inventory will be available from which to service the stores' needs. If computer-prediction methods are used, no action would be taken in most cases as long as the desired over-all level of service to stores were maintained. A short-supply report is another example of an "exception report."

7. *Vendor-performance report.* Reports on vendor performance may be compiled to show whether merchandise and delivered orders adhered to the requirements set forth in purchase orders in relation to method of shipment, time of receipt, and quantity shipped.

These reports may be correlated with reports on the number of scratches of an item, the length of time an out-of-stock condition existed, and the retail value of the lost sales.

As a result of using vendor-performance reports, a company can point out to a vendor: "Your order was received two days later than specified on the purchase order. As a result, we were out of stock of 70 cases of canned peaches. Each of us lost $380 in sales!" [4]

It is important to note that all the reports discussed above may be obtained from a computer on the basis of information given to it when each store order is shipped. When programmed to do so, a computer can produce the merchandise movement reports referred to without any input other than the one-time introduction of data on the individual items shipped out from the distribution center.

Additional reports

Other reports produced by the computer depend on additional information from the stores. Included among such reports are:

1. *Store inventory report.* The dollar value, at retail and at cost, of the shipments made to each store in the course of a week (or daily, if desired) is entered automatically on a merchandise control ledger page maintained for each store. The value of the merchandise the store is supposed to have, known as the "book value," should be equal to the sales plus the value of the actual inventory left. Any difference is attributable primarily to shrinkage and markdowns. Comparison of physical inventory with "book" inventory, as reported by the computer, permits supervisors to determine how well each store is maintaining gross margins and controlling shrinkage. (To obtain a complete picture of store inventory and gross profit, however, direct store deliveries must also be considered.)

As a by-product of the inventory report, the computer automatically calculates the gross profit earned in each store. The general practice is to make this calculation at the end of each accounting period.

2. *Store movement analysis report.* A number of companies are

[4] "Integrated Data Processing at Ralphs Grocery Company."

using the computer to prepare a store movement analysis every 26 weeks, together with shelf label control tags for accurate reordering of merchandise.

The control tags, which are self-adhesive and attach to the price molding, show, for each item, size, pack, and description, recommended space allocation, average weekly movement, and the reorder point. The reorder point is calculated by the computer from a formula that enables the store to place its order only when a full case will fit into the allocated shelf space.

In addition to permitting ordering at the most profitable stock level, the store movement analysis report serves to reduce store outs and backroom rehandling of stock.

Additional uses of the computer

Although the principal justification for use of a computer at a food distribution center is its role in helping to manage inventories, the computer has many additional uses, actual and potential, including:

1. Sales forecasting and sales analysis of direct store deliveries.
2. Studies to determine the best uses of store shelf space.
3. Maintenance and scheduling of trucks and trailers.
4. Analysis of cost per truck fleet unit.
5. Analysis of productivity per man-hour for each store.
6. Studies of sales and profits in relation to invested capital.
7. Analysis of the operation of unprofitable stores and new stores.
8. Scheduling of personnel in stores and distribution centers.
9. Studies of net profit per customer and per product item.
10. Recording of store overhead as a percentage of sales and as a percentage of assets or invested capital.
11. Payroll, accounts receivable, accounts payable, and general ledger entries and analysis.
12. Evaluation of potential store location sites.
13. Scheduling of store construction.
14. Scheduling of promotional activities.
15. Determining the number of cash registers required at a store at various times throughout the day.
16. Direct communication with a computer by buyers who will be able to get information on inventory levels, prices, merchandise in transit, and problem items more quickly than they can look up the facts in written records.

The future

Future uses of computers will be closely related to the operation of supermarkets. Although it is impossible to predict precisely how they will be employed, the general direction of development is clear.

The computer will link the supermarket to the food distribution center. It will also link the food distribution center to its vendors.

Direct transmission of store requirements to the distribution center will reduce inventory requirements in relation to sales, further reduce the need for store backrooms, and increase the stores' ability to serve their customers more effectively.

Direct transmission of distribution centers' requirements to vendors will increase turnover, decrease inventory requirements in relation to shipments, reduce space requirements in relation to shipments, and increase the centers' ability to service the stores.

ORDER SELECTION

Order selection is the costliest and most important warehouse function, and requires the most personnel. If order filling falls behind, it has serious effects not only on delivery operations but on store sales as well.

That is why the food distribution center, in keeping with its basic requirement of servicing stores, pays special attention to the day-in, day-out, smooth, orderly administration of ordering and selection.

The entire selection process is designed to assemble orders in accordance with a schedule so that each store will receive the merchandise it needs on a specific day and, within reasonable limits, at a specific time on that day.

The selection process is also designed to produce a smooth flow of completed orders, thus assisting the transportation department to load and dispatch its trucks in an orderly fashion and to make the best possible use of its available manpower, equipment and dock space.

Filling the store order

The orderly, efficient selection of orders plays a key role in the entire coordinated process that results in stores receiving the merchandise they need at the time they need it.

When a store order is received at the distribution center, a computer or tabulating equipment "reshuffles" the items on that order. It then produces a list arranged in the same sequence as the slots along the aisles where the merchandise is stored to await selection. The order selector works from this list, which shows each item ordered and the quantity desired.

Exhibit 13. Store Order Converted into Warehouse Picking Order

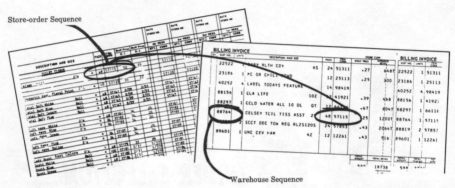

Items are listed on store order sheets in a sequence that makes it convenient for stores to write their orders. In the distribution center, the sequence in which items are listed is changed to make it convenient for order fillers to select merchandise.

Each slot has a number placed where it may be read easily by the selector. The number of the slot where an item is stored also appears on the selection list. The selector, therefore, need only match the number on the selection list with the number on the slot in order to identify the specific item ordered. Because he does not have to stop to identify the item by name or size, he saves considerable time as he moves along the selection aisle.

When the selector works his way along a predetermined path, he passes all the slots in his working area and is therefore unlikely to fail to select an ordered item if it is in its proper slot.

Because he is picking items in an orderly fashion, he need not retrace his steps and consequently can select the required items in less time than if he were to follow some random path.

Moreover, repetition of the act of selecting the same items in the same sequence familiarizes the selector with his task, and he can thus perform his work more efficiently.

One selector may pick the items needed to fill an entire store order (except for bulk and repack merchandise) or only part of a store order, depending on the system used. Chapter 7 describes the basic selection systems.

Out of stock conditions

If an item is not in the slot assigned to it, there are four possibilities:

1. *Merchandise is in the wrong slot.* This occurs only rarely. A floor plan showing where each item belongs guides stock workers as they move merchandise into the selection area. The new merchandise may be brought directly from the receiving dock to the selection area, or it may be held in a reserve stock area and then brought to the selection area as it is needed to replenish the selection slots.

2. *Merchandise is in the reserve stock area.* It is the duty of the reserve stock workers to replenish the selection slots by moving pallet loads of merchandise from the reserve to the selection area as the selection-line merchandise is worked down. They know when to do this primarily by making periodic inspections of the selection area.

If a reserve-stock worker fails to replenish an item in the selection area, he may receive the equivalent of a demerit. If he receives too many demerits, he will be required to explain why he allowed slots to remain empty. In some companies, the reserve-stock worker is responsible for filling that portion of a store order that the selector was unable to fill because some of the items were not in the selection slots.

3. *Merchandise is in the receiving area.* On rare occasions, an item may be in the process of being received and may therefore not be available elsewhere in the distribution center.

4. *Merchandise is not in the distribution center.* Because of delays in the delivery of incoming shipments, unanticipated high demand, errors in ordering or discontinuation of items, merchandise needed to fill a store order may not be in the distribution center.

The data processing system will generally determine that fact during the process of converting the store order into the merchandise picking list. Thus, the item will have been scratched as the list was being printed. The stores may have standing instructions to reorder scratched items, unless they were discontinued. In some cases, the data processing system may automatically back-order those items so that they will be added to the next shipment.

A food distribution center that has a very small percentage of scratches of items that should have been available is doing its work efficiently and is servicing its stores effectively. That center maintains a high service level.

If the number of items shipped to each store were to be only 50 percent of the total number of items ordered, the stores would obviously not be serviced properly. On the other hand, it is impossible to ship 100 percent of the items ordered because an unlimited inventory would be needed in the distribution center.

A service level of about 95 percent of the items ordered is maintained by many food distribution centers. The service level percentage, applied to the number of items shipped, is a useful measure of the efficiency of a system of supplying wanted merchandise to stores.

Service level may also be measured in terms of dollar value of merchandise shipped as a percentage of dollar value of merchandise ordered by the stores. A dollar service level is useful as a measure of the efficiency of a system of ordering merchandise from suppliers for shipment to a distribution center.

A dollar service level of 95 percent would not necessarily be equal to an item service level of 95 percent. A case of 24 No. 2½ cans of asparagus, for example, would have more than twice the value of a case of 24 No. 2½ cans of green beans, yet each case would represent one unit of merchandise. Since there are many more moderate-priced items than high-priced items, the opportunity to be out of stock on moderate-priced items is greater. Further, high-priced items tend to be slow movers and, as such, generally have to be ordered in quantities that exceed normal requirements; hence they are less likely to be out of stock.

In practice, therefore, a dollar service level of 95 percent would generally correspond to an item service level of somewhat less than 95 percent. Dollar service levels up to 98.5 percent are maintained by distribution centers with modern computer-forecasting systems.

To take care of every possible demand by stores and at the same time to guard against the possibility of delays in incoming shipments, a distribution center would have to maintain an impossibly high inventory, requiring a tremendous investment in dollars and space. An occasional scratch is inevitable. Efforts to maintain a 100 percent service level would work to the disadvantage of the total company operation. The goal of the distribution center should be to try to service the stores with as many ordered items as possible, consistent with maximum profitability.

Ordering-selection-shipping cycle

A food distribution center follows a carefully planned ordering-selection-shipping cycle. The most common cycle calls for delivery of an order within 24 hours after the order is received at the distribution center. To achieve this smooth flow of order selection and delivery, seven basic requirements must be met.

1. Store orders must be received at the warehouse on a regularly scheduled basis. Orders that come in late from stores interfere with the maintenance of the selection and delivery schedule for all stores.

2. Store orders must be converted into selection lists as part of a smoothly operated routine of data processing.

3. If a store order is to be divided among several order selectors, each portion of the order should call for approximately the same number of items. If each selector takes an equal amount of time to fill his portion of the store order, all parts of the completed order will arrive at the staging area at about the same time. Thus, all the items intended for one particular truck will be ready for loading in one operation.

4. Items selected from the bulk storage area and the repack room should arrive at the staging area at about the same time as the rest of the store's order.

5. The over-the-road vehicle needed for the load should be ready and waiting at the loading dock so that the order may be placed on it in the shortest possible time and so that the loading area may be cleared for the assembling of additional store orders.

6. If a trailer is to carry a mixed load, all the merchandise should be assembled on a schedule that will permit the trailer to be loaded quickly and efficiently. Mixed loads may include dry groceries and produce; produce and meats; meats and frozen foods; meats, delicatessen and dairy products, or other combinations of commodity lines. Since various commodity lines are selected from different areas in a distribution center, having them ready for loading at about the same time requires careful planning.

7. If a trailer is to transport loads for more than one store, the orders for all stores involved should be ready to be loaded at about the same time. The orders are loaded in the reverse sequence in which they are to be delivered.

If these activities fail to mesh, the result can be a serious breakdown in the order-filling schedule. Delays in shipping can lead to further delays at the stores. If merchandise does not arrive on schedule, store personnel ready to unload vehicles will have little work to do.

The emphasis, then, is on coordination. Without proper coordination, staging areas and loading docks can become alternately underused and overused. Order selectors can be alternately underworked and overworked. Periods of comparative idleness may be followed by periods in which overtime rates must be paid.

The most serious result of lack of coordination, of course, is that stores are not properly serviced. Since the entire purpose of a food distribution center is to service the stores, distribution executives are continually concerned with maintaining a smoothly coordinated flow of merchandise into, through, and out of the distribution center.

Standard orders

Efforts to simplify store ordering through standardization of orders have not been successful, except for meats and health and beauty aids. Store demand varies widely not only from store to store, but also from week to week within each store. Consequently, a standard (or modular) order consisting of a list of items that would be automatically reordered, would not adequately fill the needs of a store.

However, automatic reordering systems, based on standard orders, would simplify the work of the distribution center and would save considerable time in the preparation of store orders. For these reasons, distribution center executives have not ruled out the standard order as a future possibility.

The standard order has been adopted for dry groceries by some companies for emergency situations. If a single standard delivery, made under emergency conditions, is not precisely suited to the needs of an individual store, little is lost and much is gained, as the store is able to continue in business.

As the potential of modern electronic data processing is further explored by food distribution executives, modular orders may be adjusted automatically for each store on the basis of reports of individual item movement, through point-of-purchase recording of the sales. Such variation of the modular order idea must wait, however, until various kinds of equipment are perfected and the economic justification for their use is demonstrated.

11

TRANSPORTATION: THE LINK BETWEEN CENTER AND STORE

So that the correct merchandise may be delivered from the distribution center to the store at the right time, the transportation function must mesh with the store ordering-selection-shipping cycle.

After merchandise is selected for a store order, it is shipped from the distribution center to the store in two principal ways: in straight loads and in mixed loads.

When one line of commodities, such as dry groceries, fills an entire trailer, the shipment is said to be a *straight load*. The shipment may be destined for a single store or for several stores.

When two or more lines of commodities, such as produce, dairy products, and meats, are combined to fill an entire trailer, the shipment is said to be a *mixed load*. (A mixed load is sometimes called a combination load.) The shipment is usually intended for a single store. Dry groceries may be combined with other lines of commodities to form a mixed load.

Most stores place a dry groceries order twice a week. For a large store, each order would usually be large enough to require a full trailer load of merchandise. An average-size supermarket, however, generally requires one full trailer load for its first order, and only about one-half a trailer load for its second order of the week. The truck making the second delivery would therefore be carrying orders for more than one store.

Similarly, an order for one line of perishables such as meats, even for a large store, is seldom sufficient to fill a trailer, so that a straight load of meats would normally be intended for several stores.

Food distribution centers give considerable thought to the problem of when to schedule a straight load and when to schedule a mixed load. The advantages and disadvantages of each method must be weighed carefully in each specific set of circumstances.

Straight loads

The advantages of shipping straight loads are:

1. The order is assembled from only one section of the distribution center and may be loaded quickly onto a waiting trailer without having to be merged with merchandise from other sections of the distribution center.

2. A straight load of dry groceries does not require expensive cooling equipment and insulation on the trailer. If necessary, however, it can be shipped in a trailer equipped for cooling, thus giving the distribution center a wider choice of vehicles in the event of equipment breakdown.

3. A straight load of dry groceries may be so stowed that there is little unused space, because of the regular shape of grocery cases.

4. If only dry groceries are shipped, the tightly packed load of heavy cases comes close to the maximum weight capacity of the vehicle. Truck efficiency is maximized because it is measured by the number of ton-miles (tons × miles) recorded.

5. A straight load of dry groceries can be loaded and unloaded faster than a mixed load of dry groceries and perishables, since dry groceries can withstand somewhat rougher handling than a mixed load and are more regular in shape.

The disadvantages of shipping straight loads are:

1. A truck must make more than one stop if the load is too big for one store. This is a disadvantage as more time is needed to dispose of a total load to two or three stores than when an entire load is delivered to a single store. When a single stop is made, such operations as maneuvering the vehicle to the unloading point at the store, opening and closing the trailer doors, and preparing to unload the shipment are performed only once; when several stops are made, these operations must be duplicated at each stop. Thus, the total time spent in unloading a given quantity of merchandise is less when one stop is made than when several stops are made.

2. Moreover, when several stops are made, the time of arrival at each successive stop depends largely on the efficiency with which the unloading was performed at each previous stop. Thus, the second or third store on the route may find it difficult to plan personnel schedules and may sustain added costs by having people on hand too soon. This will tend to increase store personnel costs.

3. The delivery of a straight load divided among several stores requires more total vehicle mileage than the delivery of a mixed load destined for a single store, and results in greater transportation expense.

Mixed loads

The advantages of shipping mixed loads are:

1. Because a mixed load is usually intended for one store and only one stop need be made, transportation costs are lowered. Moreover, the flexibility allowed in making up a mixed load helps the transportation department to supply efficient service to the stores at no additional expense. For example, if Wednesday calls for the heaviest meat deliveries, the orders for ice cream or frozen foods might be cut back from the Wednesday deliveries for all or some of the stores and sent out with the next delivery. If Monday is a heavy produce day, some other products might be omitted from Monday deliveries. To smooth out peaks and valleys in delivery, mixed loads may be balanced out over the week, with the cooperation of the store operating people.

2. Mixed loads help to use equipment more effectively than straight loads by reducing the mileage necessary to deliver comparable amounts of merchandise. At first glance, it may appear that little can be done to reduce total mileage, since the stores are at fixed distances from the distribution center. However, careful scheduling and the combining of various types of items into single loads can reduce the total mileage traveled.

For example, Store A and Store B each takes one-half trailer load of produce and dairy products and another one-half trailer load of meat. Store A is 50 miles from the distribution center, and Store B, continuing in a straight line, is 100 miles from the distribution center.

If a full trailer load of produce and dairy products is sent to Store A, where half the load is dropped, and is then sent to Store B, where the remainder of the load is delivered, the round trip will total 200 miles. When the process is repeated, with a full trailer load of meat, an additional 200 miles will be traveled. The total mileage for both trips is 400 miles.

However, if a combination load of meat and produce-dairy is sent

Exhibit 14. How Combination Loading May Reduce Mileage

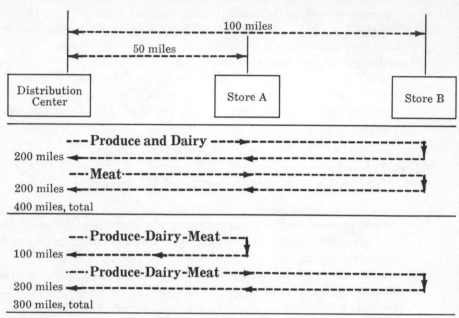

When one trailer is loaded with produce-dairy for two stores, total distance is 200 miles. A second trailer loaded with meat for the two stores travels another 200 miles. By combining produce-dairy and meat on a single trailer, the delivery for the first store requires only 100 miles of travel. A second trailer, with a combined load of produce-dairy and meat, travels 200 miles. In the first case, a total of 400 miles is traveled; in the second case, a total of only 300 miles is traveled.

to Store A, the vehicle will travel 100 miles round trip. A second combination load of meat and produce-dairy, sent to Store B, will travel 200 miles round trip.

The total mileage for both trips is 300 miles, a saving of 25 percent in mileage, with exactly the same result accomplished in delivering the necessary products to Stores A and B. (See Exhibit 14.)

The disadvantages of shipping mixed loads are:

1. If stores are clustered relatively near the distribution center, the mileage saved by shipping mixed loads is not very great. In that case, the many advantages of shipping straight loads outweigh the advantages of shipping mixed loads.

2. To avoid sending out a truck that is only partially filled, additional merchandise must be sent along even though the store may not need it. This is more likely to occur with mixed loads than with straight loads, because of the difficulty in coordinating such shipments.

Timing deliveries

The timing of deliveries with respect to both days of the week and hours of the day requires careful coordination. At the food distribution center, a dispatcher is in charge of fulfilling the schedules designed to make the most efficient use of man power and equipment while giving the stores the best possible service.

For maximum use of equipment as well as for the convenience of the stores, a general practice is to deliver dry groceries in the daytime and produce, dairy, bread, and other perishables at night. The perishables arrive at the store prior to opening time and may be processed and placed on display early.

"Using this system," says the distribution director of a major food chain, "we are able to get better utilization of our automotive equipment and, at the same time, give the stores deliveries at the times they prefer."

Increasingly, food distribution centers are posting rigid schedules for the timing of deliveries. In some cases, they telephone stores in advance to remind them to get ready to receive loads.

One company makes it a practice to review its delivery schedule every week. A warehouse representative and a store operations representative meet to make the necessary revisions.

Transportation costs

The cost of delivering merchandise from distribution center to stores varies from company to company. The ways in which various companies measure their transportation costs also differ. Consequently, it is difficult to compare costs and set up guidelines indicating what these costs should be. It is therefore important to have an understanding of the many factors affecting transportation costs and to give each one its proper emphasis.

Major factors causing variations in transportation costs are:

Exhibit 15. Daily Dispatch Sheet

DAILY DISPATCH SHEET

______________DIVISION

DATE

TRACTOR OR TRUCK	MAKE	DRIVER	HELPER	TRAILER NUMBER	LOADING TIME		TIME			STOPS			KIND LOAD	WEIGHT	MILES TRAVELED	INBOUND			GARAGE		
					START	FINISH	OUT	IN	TOTAL	FIRST	LAST	TOTAL				TIME OUT	TIME IN	WEIGHT	TIME IN	TIME OUT	

Information on all truck runs is recapitulated to provide a permanent record of work performed.

1. *The type of load carried.* Heavy, dense merchandise costs less to carry per hundredweight than light merchandise, because more weight can be packed into a given space. Thus, dry groceries cost less to carry per hundredweight than all other commodities. Produce costs about 60 percent more per hundredweight than dry groceries, and meat about 56 percent more than produce, with baked goods about 40 percent more than meat.

2. *The value of the load.* Meat, for example, has a very high value

Exhibit 16. Truck Hauling Route Sheet

TRUCK HAULING ROUTE SHEET

Driver				Date 19
Helper				Route
Starting Time	A.M. P.M.	Leave Whse.	A.M. P.M.	Truck or Tractor No.
Quitting Time	A.M. P.M.	Return Whse.	A.M. P.M.	Trailer No.-Outbound
No. of Stops		Coffee Stop	A.M. P.M.	Trailer No.-Inbound
Lunch Time	A.M. P.M.	To	A.M. P.M.	Meter Reading-End of Trip
Total Del. Time	Hrs.	Avg. Lbs. P.H.		Meter Reading-Start of Trip
Total Driving Time	Hrs.	Avg. M.P.H.		Total Trip Miles
Garage Time	A.M. P.M.	To	A.M. P.M.	OHIO MILES – This section for Divisions with tractor-trailer hauls in Ohio
Delays				No Trailer ☐
				One Axle Trailer ☐
				Two Axle Trailer ☐
				Miles Outside of Ohio

STORE DELIVERY

Store No.	Type of Mdse.	Total Weight	Arrive	Leave	Piece Count	Manager's Signature

STORE HAULING TOTALS

Grocery	
Bread	
Milk	
Frozen Food	
Ice Cream	
Produce	
Meat	
Total Weight	
Salvage % Load	%

INTER-DIVISION HAULING

Description	Trailer Outbound	Trailer Inbound	Weight	Time Arrived	Time They Arrived	Time Leaving
				A.M. P.M.	A.M. P.M.	A.M. P.M.
				A.M. P.M.	A.M. P.M.	A.M. P.M.
				A.M. P.M.	A.M. P.M.	A.M. P.M.
				A.M. P.M.	A.M. P.M.	A.M. P.M.

Dispatcher fills in pertinent information for the driver (store number, weight, tractor weight, piece count, etc.) and driver fills in times of arriving at stores and leaving them, mileage data and related information.

per hundredweight in comparison with produce. Thus, transportation cost as a percentage of value is lower for meat than for produce.

3. *The size of the load.* A driver is paid at the same hourly rate whether his vehicle hauls a capacity load or a less-than-capacity load; also, the cost of the equipment is unchanged. The same basic dollar cost of transportation charged against a big load, compared with a smaller load, results in a smaller charge as a percentage of the total weight carried.

4. *Traffic conditions.* Uninterrupted suburban runs for loads of dry groceries averaging 30,000 pounds are estimated to cost about 26 to 30 cents a mile, while city runs under adverse traffic conditions cost about 55 cents a mile. Stop-and-go driving requires more time to cover the same distance than does uninterrupted, over-the-road driving.

5. *The nature of the terrain.* Many companies estimate that average speed for tractors and trailers is 35 miles an hour over good country roads. Hills, narrow roads, and poorly maintained roads reduce average speed. Turnpike and expressway driving increase average speed. Low average speeds increase operating cost, while high average speeds reduce operating cost.

6. *Geographical location.* Wage rates and traffic conditions vary in different sections of the country. Broadly speaking, distances between stores also vary by geographical area. Consequently, the costs of transportation in one section of the country tend to differ from those in another section.

For example, transportation costs for food chains with sales above $100 million averaged 1.09 percent of sales in the Northeast, 0.61 in the South, and 0.74 in the Midwest, according to a Cornell University study.[1]

7. *The type of equipment used.* The investment in equipment and the annual amount that must be charged off to pay for the equipment (depreciation and interest) vary. According to leading food companies, the typical cost of a fully equipped diesel tractor is $18,000. This type of diesel tractor has the capacity (73,000 pounds gross vehicular weight) to pull a maximum load of 40,000 pounds in 40-foot tandem trailers, plus the weight of tractor and trailer (estimated to be 33,000 pounds). Each trailer would, typically, cost $9,000.

However, some companies maintain two trailers per tractor, some one and one-half trailers per tractor, and others one trailer per tractor. Assuming that the type of equipment described is in use, the investment may range from $27,000 for a tractor and one trailer to $36,000 for a tractor with two trailers, multiplied by as many tractors as are in operation. Tractors and trailers of different capacities carry dif-

[1] *1964-1965 Operating Results of Food Chains*, by Wendell Earle and John Sheehan, Cornell University, 1965.

Exhibit 17. Driver's Log

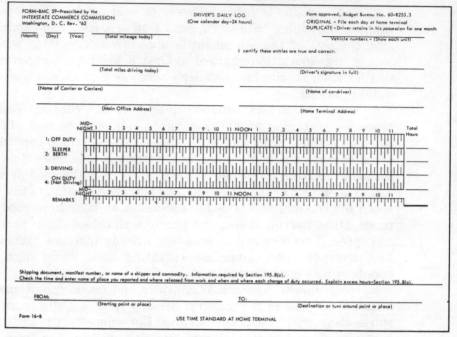

A record of each trip must be maintained by every driver.

ferent price tags. Thus, a major factor in computing transportation cost—the cost of the over-the-road equipment—may vary considerably from company to company.

8. *The capacity of the equipment.* State laws vary with respect to the weight of the maximum permissible load and the permissible length and width of the trailer. In general, the larger the permissible load, the lower the cost of transporting each unit of merchandise.

9. *How the equipment is used.* If one company confines its deliveries to stores to the daytime hours, while another company delivers during the night as well as during the day, the second company would obviously be using its equipment more extensively and would require considerably less equipment to deliver the same total tonnage.

10. *The method of loading and unloading.* When a trailer is loaded and unloaded by hand, fewer cases are handled per man-hour than when it is loaded and unloaded with the help of mechanical equipment such as conveyors or fork-lift trucks. Thus, the cost of labor for loading and unloading is reduced when mechanical equipment is used to assist in the operation. Speedier loading and unloading also result in more productive use of drivers, tractors, and trailers.

Exhibit 18. Transportation Costs

ACTUAL		BUDGET			Transportation MWT-11	ACTUAL		BUDGET	
				76/3121	Salaries - Super.& Office				
				3199	- Super. Transfer				
					Sub Total-Supervn. (A)				
				76/3131	Salaries - Drivers				
				3138	- Drivers Vacation				
				3198	- Drivers Trans.				
					Sub Total Drivers (B)				
				76/3143	Salaries - Janitors				
				3151	- Wash, Gas., & Mech.				
				3152	- Reefer Mech.				
				3311	Vehicle Rental				
				3321	Tires & Tubes				
				3322	Veh., & Shop Supplies				
				3331	Gasoline				
				3333	Oil & Grease				
				3334	Liquid Nitrogen				
				3341	Depreciation				
				3351	Mechanical Repairs & Pts.				
				3352	Body Repairs & Paint				
				3354	Reefer Repairs & Parts				
				3364	Vehicle Licenses				
				3399	Maintenance Credits				
				3410	Site Improvements				
				3419	Rent - Co.owned Bldg.				
				3421	Outside Guard Service				
				3425	Hse.Keeping & Off. Supplies				
				3429	Outside E.D.P. Services				
				3431	Utility Costs				
				3463	Personal Property Tax				
				3476	Insp. Fines & Fees				
					Sub Total Operating (C)				
				3137	Safety Awards & Educ.				
				3461	Taxes - Payroll				
				3471	Insurance				
				3472	Package Plan				
				3482	Health & Welfare				
				3621	Travel				
				3995	Admin. Charges				
					Sub Total - Other (D)				
				3931	Other Handling Credits				
				3932	Supplier Pickup Credits				
					Sub Total Credits (E)				
					Net Transportation (A-E)				
				3312	Contract Hauling (F)				
					Gross Transp. (A-F)				

PERIOD, 19 _____   MFG., WHSING., & TRANSPORTATION   _____ PERIODS, 19 _____

The many factors that enter into total transportation expense are carefully budgeted. Actual costs are later compared with budgeted figures as a control.

11. *The number of stops made.* "Stop contact"—the time required to maneuver the truck to an unloading position, to inform store personnel of the truck's arrival, to open doors, and to prepare for unloading—has been calculated at 12 minutes per stop by a consulting firm which has set standards of transportation performance.[2] The more

[2] Drake, Sheahan, Sweeney and Hupp, New York.

Exhibit 19. How Mechanization Reduces Unloading Time

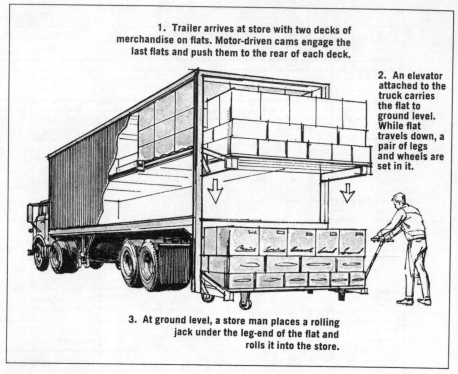

1. Trailer arrives at store with two decks of merchandise on flats. Motor-driven cams engage the last flats and push them to the rear of each deck.

2. An elevator attached to the truck carries the flat to ground level. While flat travels down, a pair of legs and wheels are set in it.

3. At ground level, a store man places a rolling jack under the leg-end of the flat and rolls it into the store.

stops a truck makes, the more "stop contact" time is required, thus adding to the cost of operation.

12. *The size of the store served.* If a store is large enough to require a 2,000-case order shipped in one trailer, the cost of serving that store would be less than the cost of serving two smaller stores, each requiring a 1,000-case order. On the other hand, a 3,000-case order is too big for one trailer or for a store to receive efficiently because it would choke the receiving area and backroom, and would require a peak number of employees to expedite unloading and handling.[3]

13. *The efficiency of maintenance procedures.* If a company follows effective methods of keeping its equipment in good operating condition, breakdowns will be avoided, fuel consumption will be minimized, and major repairs will be required only infrequently.

14. *Weather conditions.* Frequent snow, heavy rain, and extreme cold delay deliveries. Companies operating in areas with adverse weather conditions incur additional transportation costs.

Because of the complexities of calculating costs for hauling dry

[3] *Summary Report,* NAFC Clinic on Warehousing and Transportation, 1967.

groceries and various kinds of perishables, many companies use a per-hour figure as the basis for charging transportation costs to stores.

Some cost items of operating trucks vary with mileage (fuel, tires, and maintenance), but the greater proportion of expense varies with time or is fixed (drivers' wages, depreciation, licenses, supervision, rent).

The simple method of using time as the basis for charging trans-portation costs to stores is said by one large food chain to be suffi-ciently accurate for an interdepartmental charge. Dry groceries and perishables are charged at the same hourly rate. The grocery loads are heavier, but the perishables require refrigeration. For simplicity, no differentiation is made.

Because of the many variable factors that enter into calculating transportation costs, per-hour charges vary widely within this com-pany from one geographical division to another.

Transporting perishables

Perishables present a difficult technical problem in transportation from distribution centers to stores, because they must be kept at tem-peratures within somewhat rigid ranges.

Holding temperatures of $-10°F$ for ice cream, $0°F$ for frozen foods, $33°F$ to $40°F$ for meats, $38°F$ to $40°F$ for milk and cheese, and $34°F$ to $45°F$ for other perishables in the medium-temperature range are necessary for effective transportation of those commodities.

Although produce is in the perishables category, many companies ship it without refrigeration because, during much of the year, out-side temperatures add little heat to the product.

Shipping temperature-compatible products

If temperature-compatible products are shipped together (ice cream with frozen foods at $-10°F$, milk products with meat, etc.), less than a full trailer load is usually required for a single store. To fill the trailer, the orders of several stores must be shipped on the same ve-hicle. In hot weather, the opening of trailer doors to make deliveries increases the temperature inside the trailer. Normally the doors of the trailer must remain open until the order is completely off the trailer and the vehicle can be pulled away from the dock of the store.

During the unloading process, the outside air is kept from coming in contact with the product as much as possible with the use of vinyl curtains. As the driver unloads from the back of the truck, the cur-tains are moved to a position in back of the load. For side door deliv-ery, the curtain is kept across the open side door while unloading is going on.

The length of time that trailer doors are open may be reduced with the use of roll-up doors instead of hinged doors. Roll-up doors may be closed while the trailer is standing at an unloading dock. In many situations, hinged doors cannot be closed until the trailer has been pulled away from the dock to allow clearance for the doors to be swung shut.

Mechanical refrigeration is the principal method used for keeping products under temperature control, but the use of liquid nitrogen is gaining increased acceptance. Liquid nitrogen, sprayed into a compartment holding cold products, maintains them at the temperatures at which they were loaded into the vehicle; it also forms a partial protective atmosphere by displacing oxygen in the enclosed space, thus inhibiting product deterioration.

When trailer doors are opened, mechanical refrigeration must work harder to maintain the correct temperature for the balance of the run; similarly, nitrogen, lost when trailer doors are opened, must be replaced quickly for the balance of the run.

The technical problem concerning where to use mechanical refrigeration and where to use liquid nitrogen is currently under consideration by transportation executives, and many tests of equipment in use under practical conditions are being made. Generalizations tend to be misleading in the technical area. However, it may be said the need to replace nitrogen after each stop adds considerably to cost, and for this reason nitrogen will probably be used primarily to hold temperatures of loads that are delivered to single stores. But, technical advances may lead in directions that cannot now be predicted. Suffice it to say, therefore, that the development of temperature control equipment using both mechanical and chemical means will result in delivery vehicles with improved capabilities, so that the delivery of perishables will be carried on in the future even more efficiently and economically than it is now being done.

Shipping items requiring different temperatures

Perishables requiring different levels of temperature are usually shipped in the same trailer only to stores that are distant from a distribution center. Maintaining different temperatures in the same vehicle is expensive. However, the alternative of sending out two trucks results in very high mileage costs.

If perishables that require different temperatures are shipped together, provision must be made for zoned control of temperatures. This may be achieved with low-temperature containers capable of holding products at the temperatures at which they were loaded (with relatively little accumulation of heat), or with compartments within a trailer. The compartments may be built into the vehicle; for practical purposes, however, they are more likely to be formed by movable bulkheads, sealed into the sides of the trailer to prevent temperature exchange between compartments. When bulkheads are movable, a trailer may be used in a flexible manner.

Products that have been brought down to various temperatures tend to hold those temperatures for some time after they have been exposed to warmer air. The time varies, of course, with the temperature and the product. The fact that heat exchange does take some time to occur makes it possible to move perishables from cold environments through warmer environments and, again, to cold environments. However, the shorter the exposure of perishables to a warmer environment, the better the condition in which the products will be displayed and sold in the stores.

Typical of the effort made to maintain proper temperatures is the use being made by some companies of cold boxes that are transported to the store loaded with milk or ice cream, dropped outdoors at the store, and kept cold by compressors outside the store itself. Where sizable deliveries are made, outdoor cold boxes save store space, maintain the product without exposing it to outdoor temperatures, and are relatively economical to use.

Unitizing shipments

Unitized loading and unloading, discussed in Chapter 8 in connection with the *receiving* operation at the distribution center, is also an efficient procedure in connection with the *shipping* operation. It will be recalled that unitization is based on the concept that it is easier to handle several items when they are formed into a single unit than it is to handle each item individually.

Unitization is becoming increasingly important in the transportation of merchandise from distribution centers to stores. In 1959, a spot check of participants in an NAFC Warehousing and Transportation Clinic indicated that about one-half the large food retailers were using some form of unitization in making some of their deliveries to stores. A similar check at a 1967 Clinic showed that virtually every chain represented at the meeting was using some form of unitization and the consensus of the group was that unitized shipping would increase.

Various methods of combining small units to form larger units are in use. Some of the principal methods of unitization used in shipping merchandise from distribution centers to stores are:

1. *Palletization*. Order selectors at the distribution center place cases of merchandise on pallets at the time the items are selected. At the shipping dock, each pallet load of merchandise is moved into a trailer by a fork-lift truck that enters the trailer itself.

The palletized merchandise in the trailer may occupy 40 pallets

Table 19. Comparative Costs for Hand-Stacked versus Pallet-Stacked Delivery of Dry Groceries

Hypothetical case for delivering 20,000,000 pieces of dry groceries annually to 150 stores at an average distance of 25 miles from a distribution center. Calculations are based on studies made by two large food companies and data available in NAFC reports of Warehousing and Transportation Clinics.

	Hand-stacking	Pallet-stacking
1. Number of pieces loaded per man-hour.*	562	1,875
2. Number of man-hours required to load 20,000,000 pieces. (20,000,000 ÷ line 1)	35,590	10,670
3. Cost of loading @ $3.25 per man-hour.** (line 2 × $3.25)	$115,668	$34,678
4. Use of three additional fork-lift trucks @ $450 per year per truck (based on 10-year life).	—	$1,350
5. Total number of pieces delivered per trip. (Pallet-stacking averages 12.5% fewer pieces per load than hand-stacking.)	1,360	1,200
6. Total trips per vehicle per year.***	400	600
7. Annual payload (number of pieces) per vehicle. (line 5 × line 6)	544,000	720,000
8. Average round trip (miles).	50	50
9. Annual mileage per vehicle. (line 6 × line 8)	20,000	30,000
10. Total number of vehicles required. (20,000,000 pieces ÷ line 7 and rounded to nearest whole number)	37	28
11. Operating cost per mile, travel time only.	$0.25	$0.25
12. Operating cost annually, travel time only. (line 9 × line 10 × line 11)	$185,000	$210,000
13. Average time for unloading (hours), per trip.****	3.75	1.00
14. Unloading cost for vehicles and drivers annually, @ $7 per hour. (line 6 × line 10 × line 13 × $7)	$388,500	$117,600
15. Additional unloading cost with hand-stacking. (Store personnel @ $200 per year per store) (150 stores × $200)	$30,000	—
16. Use of manual pallet jacks @ $35 per year per jack (150 stores × $35).	—	$5,250
17. Use of 1,500 additional pallets @ 70 cents per year per pallet (based on 5-year life).	—	$1,050
18. Total annual cost. (lines 3, 4, 12, 14, 15, 16, 17)	$719,168	$369,928
19. Total annual saving with pallet-stacking (rounded).	—	$350,000
20. Total annual saving per store with pallet-stacking (rounded).	—	$2,333
21. Total annual saving with pallet-stacking, as a percentage of hand-stacking cost.	—	48.6%

* Based on a study by the U.S. Department of Agriculture, in *Marketing Research Report No. 94*, which concludes that hand-stacking takes about 3½ times the man-hours than does pallet-stacking with the use of a fork-lift truck to load a trailer. A number of food chains agree; they report that manual loading yields about 3 tons per man-hour vs. pallet-loading which yields more than 10 tons per man-hour.

(two across, ten deep, and two high) in a very tight load in a 40-foot trailer. However, a more general practice is to place 18 pallet loads in a 40-foot trailer (two across, nine deep, and one high) and to place additional individual items at the top—a procedure known as top-loading. Although it is possible to stow pallet loads ten deep in a 40-foot trailer, overhanging merchandise and quick stowing methods usually result in a load nine pallets deep.

Transportation executives are less concerned about top-loading (which uses more of the available cubage) for short trips than they are for long trips. For short trips, they are interested primarily in the speed with which the trailer can be loaded and unloaded. For long trips, they are primarily concerned with hauling the most merchandise per mile of travel.

At the store, the pallets are removed by the use either of a fork-lift truck or, more commonly, of a less expensive hydraulic pallet jack of 2,000 pound capacity.

A hypothetical case showing comparative costs of hand-stacking and pallet-stacking in the shipping operation is summarized in Table 19.

As Table 19 indicates, fewer cases are delivered per trip and more trips are required for delivering a given quantity of merchandise when pallet-stacked, unitized shipments are made. However, many man-hours are saved in loading and unloading the merchandise. On balance, the savings in pallet-stacking, compared with hand-stacking, may be considerable.

Exhibit 20.
Cage Is Container

The use of cages is increasing to achieve unitization of shipments from distribution centers to stores.

In the hypothetical example, a saving of 48.6 percent is enjoyed annually when pallet-stacking is used instead of hand-stacking. The average per store saving with pallet-stacked, unitized loading and unloading is $2,333.

** Cost of truck waiting time is not included since total loading time under both methods can be approximately equal, but more man-hours are required for manual-stacking.
*** Estimates of total trips per vehicle per year are based on 8 trips weekly for 50 weeks for hand-stacked vehicles and 50% more trips weekly for pallet-stacked vehicles. These estimates would vary, of course, with the total number of hours of daily operation of each vehicle.
**** Based on studies by two large food chains.

Exhibit 21. Delivering on Pallets

Trailer is loaded with double decked skids (left). At the store, an extra wheel is affixed to each skid (center). Loaded skids are mechanically lowered and driver wheels the load into the store (right).

The advantages of pallet-stacking decrease, however, as the average distance increases and the emphasis is on hauling as much merchandise as possible on a trailer.

2. *A cage on wheels.* As he selects the items, the order selector at the distribution center places cases of merchandise in a metal mesh cage on a wheeled bed. The cage forms a container which is shipped to the store, unloaded as a unit from the truck with the aid of a mechanically operated elevator tail gate, and wheeled out to the selling floor. This method of unitization is gaining rapid acceptance. Several large chains use it exclusively for all merchandise except hanging meat.

3. *Loading on skids.* Store orders are placed on platforms, called skids, as they are selected. The loaded skids are placed on rails in the trailer so that they may be slid into the trailer for loading and out of it for unloading. To unload the trailer, the skids are slid to the rear of the trailer, where a hydraulically controlled lift, which is part of the trailer's equipment, lowers them to the ground level. Wheels are then attached to the skids, which are hauled into the store with the help of a wheeled hand jack.

4. *Laundry-type hampers.* Non-foods that are crushable or are formed into odd shapes are difficult to transport unless they are placed in some kind of container such as a reusable canvas laundry-type hamper. Many non-foods take up a high volume of space in relation to weight, and are therefore difficult to ship in combination with grocery items. Equipment designed to haul dense goods—merchandise of high tonnage in relation to cubage, such as canned goods—is usually not

adaptable to the transportation of low-tonnage, high-cubage items, such as paper products, unless productivity is sacrificed.

5. *Insulated containers with retractable legs.* Some containers that can be left at the stores are built with retractable legs and in various sizes. A power unit, usually equipped with a hydraulic lift, backs under the container and raises it from the ground, enabling the legs to be either lowered or retracted into the body. These containers may be insulated, and mechanical refrigeration may be installed in them.

6. *Weather-tight containers on flat-bed trucks.* The weather-tight containers may be mounted on a flat-bed truck and can be lowered to the ground with a winch. Casters on the boxes permit them to be rolled into a store. Hydraulic tailgates may also be used to lower them to ground level. One proposal is for a trailer to carry a small fork-lift truck to be used for moving containers built on pallets instead of casters.

7. *Insulated holding boxes.* Insulated holding boxes, with no mechanical refrigeration units, are available in sizes from 40- to 60-cubic-foot capacities. Some hold ice cream up to 18 hours with only a 3 to 5 degree temperature rise, without dry ice. These boxes may be packed either inside or outside a freezer; they may be loaded on dry trailers or refrigerated trailers; and they may also be used as additional freezer space at the stores by installing mechanical refrigeration units in them. The cold boxes may be used to keep merchandise frozen on a high-temperature trailer or to keep merchandise from freezing on a low-temperature trailer. The use of cold boxes has increased the flexibility of use of over-the-road equipment in combination loading.

8. *Compartmentation.* Compartmentation is, in effect, a variety of containerization. A trailer with two compartments—one with capacity for below-zero holding and the other with capacity for holding at varying temperatures from 35 degrees for meat to 55 degrees for green produce—is in common use. A third compartment—dry space for merchandise that does not require refrigeration—may be included.

9. *The entire trailer.* An entire trailer is a container. When a trailer is dropped at a store, it may then be unloaded to meet the convenience of store management in scheduling personnel. The empty trailer is picked up when the store receives its next delivery or when a tractor is available for that purpose.

Backhauls

A food distribution center's transportation department continually seeks ways to make full use of its delivery equipment. One way in which equipment as well as man power can be put to greater effective use is to obtain return loads—called backhauls—after deliveries have been made to stores. Backhauls can account for as much as 30 per-

Exhibit 22. Pick Up Sheet

PICK UP SHEET

TRUCK OR TRACTOR NO.	DRIVER	DATE
TRAILER NO.	HELPER	

TIME		LUNCH		TOTAL MILEAGE	INDIANA MILES	TOTAL ILLINOIS MILES
START		START		FINISH		
FINISH		FINISH		START		TOTAL INDIANA MILES
				TOTAL MILES	TOTAL MILES	TOTAL MILEAGE

PICK UP NO.	BRANCH INVOLVED	PICK UP NO.	BRANCH INVOLVED
PLACE OF PICKUP		PLACE OF PICKUP	
ADDRESS		ADDRESS	
AMOUNT	COMMODITY	AMOUNT	COMMODITY

DRIVERS - FILL BELOW

BRAND NAME		BRAND NAME	
SHIPPER		SHIPPER	
NO. OF CASES		NO. OF CASES	
WEIGHT		WEIGHT	
TIME IN	TIME OUT	TIME IN	TIME OUT
SEAL NO'S.		SEAL NO'S.	

REASONS FOR ANY DELAYS

DO NOT FILL
REVENUE
COST
PROFIT

Backhauls bring revenue to many companies, partially offsetting the cost of operating their transportation departments. Pick up sheet is used to enter details on each trip on which backhauls were carried.

cent of a company's total tonnage hauled in its own carriers.

Customers who haul their own merchandise are compensated by suppliers at prevailing freight rates, and the net income from backhauls offsets part of the cost of operating a transportation department. Every backhaul tends to reduce a company's net charge for service to the stores. Although no industry-wide studies have been made on backhauls, the consensus of informed transportation executives places savings at about $2,000 per truck per year.

Virtually every distribution center has some backhauls available to it.

Traffic functions

The transportation departments of larger companies are usually responsible for performing certain traffic functions. These relate to inbound freight: how it is shipped, routing, and claims for damage, as well as programs to reduce shipping costs and to eliminate the causes of damage to merchandise.

Exhibit 23. Driver Report
of Vehicle Condition

DRIVER REPORT OF VEHICLE CONDITION				
TRACTOR:		TRAILER:		
SPEEDOMETER READING:		DATE		

ENGINE	NO POWER		STEER-ING	HARD STEERING	
	NOISY			WANDER	
	OVERHEATING			FREE PLAY	
	LOW OIL PRESSURE		BRAKES	AIR LEAKS	
	WATER LEAKS			SERVICE	
	OIL LEAKS			PARKING	
CLUTCH	SLIPPING		DRIVE LINE	NOISY	
	GRABBING			VIBRATES	
	POOR RELEASE				
TRANSMISSION			MISCELLANEOUS	TIRES	
	NOISY			BATTERY	
	DOES NOT STAY IN GEAR			STARTER	
	HARD TO SHIFT			GENERATOR	
	OIL LEAKS			LIGHTS	
				WINDSHIELD WIPER	
				EXHAUST LEAKS	
REAR AXLE	NOISY			FUEL LEAKS	
	OIL LEAKS			REEFER	
	INCORRECT SHIFTING			FLAGS OR FLARES	
				FIRE EXTINGUISHER	

EXPLAIN OTHER MALFUNCTIONS:

_____

_____

_____

_____

TRAILER REMARKS:

_____

_____

_____

SIGNATURE_____

After each trip, driver fills out report which is reviewed by garage foreman so that corrective action may be taken when necessary.

Maintenance

The proper maintenance of tractors, trailers, and straight trucks is vital to the continuity of service to stores. The quality of maintenance is directly related to the amount of downtime—time during which equipment cannot be used because it is being repaired. Rigidly enforced preventive maintenance, regularly scheduled overhauls, comprehensive driver reports on each truck after each trip, and immediate shop follow-through on all complaints listed by drivers result in high-quality maintenance, which, in turn, results in minimum idle time for equipment.

New programs are now available that tie in maintenance with computer record-keeping and signaling to indicate when each maintenance function should be performed, thus providing a peripheral use for computers already installed by food companies for other purposes.

Over-the-road equipment presents a company image to the public. Attractive lettering on the sides of the trailers and top-notch maintenance, including washing and repainting, help to make rolling billboards of tractors and trailers; this is an important part of a company's public relations program.

Purchasing or leasing equipment

Determining whether to purchase or to lease over-the-road equipment is a basic function of the transportation department. Most over-the-road equipment used by food distribution centers is owned and operated by the centers. In some cases, however, equipment is leased. Some companies lease only tractors; others lease both tractors and trailers. Some use the leasing organization's drivers; others use their own.

Some companies own sufficient equipment to handle their normal loads and then lease additional equipment to handle occasional peak loads.

Inter-department coordination

A transportation department can be of maximum service to stores when its work is coordinated with that of other operating departments. At the 1967 NAFC Warehousing and Transportation Clinic, great stress was placed on the concept of total coordination.

For example, the transportation department works with the store planning department to design receiving docks and doors to specifications that will speed the receiving operation at the stores. The location of coolers, the installation of cages to hold night deliveries, and the proportion of store space used for storage are other problems on which the transportation department may be consulted.

When the transportation and store operating departments cooperate, costs can be cut significantly and service improved.

The future development of the transportation function to serve the food industry will undoubtedly stress the continuity of operations from source to consumer. One step now being taken in that direction is the application of the computer to the solution of problems of scheduling, determining optimum loads, and using minimum equipment and man power while rendering maximum service.

However, increased efficiency in transportation alone is not the goal. It is in devising the best methods of coordinating efficient transportation with efficient warehousing and store operation that the challenge of the future lies.

12 FRESH MEATS

A successful fresh meat department stabilizes an entire store operation. Meats account for about 25 percent of total supermarket volume and, from 1962 through 1965, shoppers listed the quality and freshness of meats as the most important factors in selecting a favorite supermarket.[1] In 1966, meat shared first place with "low prices on groceries" in the selection of a favorite supermarket.

Maintaining the profitability of the meat department is a major goal of every supermarket. The method of distribution of meats affects profitability to a marked degree.

The two basic methods of distribution are through (1) direct store delivery and (2) a company's food distribution center.

Direct store deliveries

Items delivered directly from the packer to the store, bypassing a company's own warehouse, include sides, quarters, and primal cuts of beef; lamb carcasses, and pork in primal cuts. Store personnel must then break down these cuts into retail cuts.

Experiments are being conducted with boxed cuts from packers, re-

[1] Burgoyne Index, Inc., *Annual Study of Supermarket Shoppers.*

ducing the amount of processing required at store level. So-called block cuts are trimmed primals, boxed for shipment. While tests are still in the experimental stage, it is claimed that direct delivery of trimmed primal cuts—wrapped, boxed, and unitized—from packing plant to retail store, provides savings in store labor expense. Cuts of smaller proportions are being boxed experimentally also. A variety package containing flank steak, skirt steak, trimmed shank, and trimmed brisket is being tested.

The general practice today, however, is to deliver packers' cuts that must be broken down at the store.

Advantages of direct delivery
Direct store delivery of meats has the following advantages:

1. It eliminates the need for a company to invest in warehouse space and equipment for storage and processing of the product and in trucks to transport it.

2. Proponents of this method of distribution claim that there is less shrinkage if a packer's cut is processed close to the point of sale than if it is broken into primal or retail cuts at a warehouse. To the extent that direct deliveries reduce the number of days in the cycle from slaughter to sales, shrinkage is reduced. Fresh beef, for example, loses about 1/2 of 1 percent of its weight per day in shrink.

Disadvantages of direct delivery
Direct store delivery of meats has the following disadvantages:

Table 20. Weekly Direct Store

Store Operations of Less Than 11 Units

Meat Sales Volume in Thousands of Dollars	2-3	3-5	5-7.5	7.5-10	10-15	15 & Over	Average
Average Number Deliveries per Week	16	21	21	29	25	41	23
Average Tonnage per Delivery	280	385	500	530	890	870	575
Percent Deliveries under 300 Lbs.	69	64	54	53	42	44	54

American Meat Institute

Conventional method of store processing requires a high number of weekly deliveries. Study by American Meat Institute indicates that as volume increases so does the average number of deliveries per store. Average tonnage per delivery also increases with the rise in meat sales volume, moving from about 300 pounds

1. Upwards of 30 deliveries per week per store may be required when meat is received direct from packers. A study by the American Meat Institute shows that 16 out of every 30 direct deliveries of meat are of less than 300 pounds (Table 20). This disadvantage is overcome when a packer provides a variety of types of meats and delivers them in one truck to fill a store's order, but such an arrangement is not common.

2. All shipments must be inspected and weight-checked at the store.

Deliveries through a food distribution center

Delivery through a company's food distribution center may take one of three forms:

1. Meats may be assembled from various packers and selected and shipped to meet store requirements, without being processed at the distribution center. Store personnel must then break them down in much the same way as if they had been delivered directly from the packers.

2. Sides and quarters that move through a company's food distribution center may be broken down into wholesale or primal cuts. This is a common method of moving meats through company-operated distribution centers. Currently, the major emphasis is on processing the product into primal cuts, which are then shipped to stores for further processing into retail cuts.

Deliveries of Meat from Packers

Store Operations of More Than 10 Units

Meat Sales Volume in Thousands of Dollars	2-3	3-5	5-7.5	7.5-10	10-15	15 & Over	Average
Average Number Deliveries per Week	19	21	26	28	34	33	30
Average Tonnage per Delivery	300	300	485	650	670	1100	660
Percent Deliveries under 300 Lbs.	84	73	57	50	50	36	53

in the $2,000-to-$3,000-per-week store to 1,100 pounds in the $15,000-per-week store. A significant percentage of deliveries is made in less than 300 pounds of product. As store volume increases, the frequency of small deliveries (under 300 pounds) decreases, but the over-all average is nevertheless 53 percent of total deliveries. Thus, 16 out of every 30 deliveries were under 300 pounds.

A combination of method 1 and method 2 is employed by most companies.

3. A few companies are breaking down primal cuts into retail cuts at their food distribution centers, or are planning to do so in the near future. Eventually, many corporate, voluntary, and cooperative chains expect to set up central meat plants in which meats will be processed into retail cuts and prepackaged and price-marked for shipment to stores, where they will be placed on sale without further processing.

Functions performed at the center

When meat is delivered through a company's own distribution center, the following basic functions are performed at the center:

1. *Receiving.* Weights of incoming merchandise are checked. Ideally, to prevent muffler exhaust from trucks penetrating the plant, trucks may back into air seals that connect the truck interiors directly with the loading dock. Meats may be unloaded directly into a temperature-controlled environment (free from polluted air), so that both truck and dock temperatures are better maintained.

2. *Inspection.* A highly skilled inspector checks incoming meats for quality and grade and rejects those which are not up to standard.

3. *Storage.* Beef may be stored at 36°F and pork at 34°F. Beef is stored at high relative humidity to keep it from discoloring, to hold shrinkage down, and to maintain firmness. The movement of air, playing over the exposed faces of meat, accelerates shrinkage. Consequently, air is supplied through convection rather than through forced draught in storage areas.

Chicken is held in a separate room from meats, and the gases generated by chicken are released through outside vents.

4. *Processing.* The most common processing activity in company-owned meat distribution centers is the breakdown of beef into primal cuts. Since 40°F is the critical point at which the growth of bacteria can be controlled by temperature in beef, preparation areas are held at that level. Temperature control at a central facility is vital, as large quantities of meat, distributed to many outlets, are involved.

If a distribution center breaks meat down further into retail cuts, prepackaging and price marking are performed centrally.

5. *Order selection.* Store meat orders are generally noted on simple forms and, in some cases, are telephoned in to the distribution center. A meat warehouse order sheet requires only a single large form (see Exhibit 24), since the total number of items is very small in comparison to dry groceries, for which detailed order forms are required. Data processing is used primarily for analysis of meat movement

Exhibit 24. Meat Warehouse Order

	WEIGHT EXTENSION					FILLED BY	

MEAT SECTION STAMP HERE

CODE		SECTION B	SHPD.	CODE	PKGS. PCES.	SECTION B	SHPD.	CODE
		POULTRY				**BACON**		
400		Breasts 5#		476		Briggs 12-1#		56?
401		Legs 5#		477		Briggs 24-8 oz		56?
402		Wings 5#		478		Briggs Thick Slice 6-2#		564
403		Necks, Backs 5#		479				565
404		Gizzard & Hearts 5#		480		Black Hawk 12-1#		566
405		Livers 5#		481		Black Hawk 24-8 oz		
406				482		Swifts 20-1#		570
407		Chicken Fat 6-1#		483		Swifts 24-8 oz		571
408				484		Fri-Pan 20-1#		572
409		Cornish Game Hens, 1 Pc 14 oz		485				573
410		Raw Turkey Roll 1 Pc		486		Todd Old Va. 12-1#		574
411		Turkey Wing 5#		487		Esskay 12-8 oz		575
412		Turkey Tra-Pak Drumsticks 9#		488		Jordan 12-1#		576
413		Cooked Turkey Roll 1 Pc		489		Esskay 6-1#		577
414		Turkey Tra-Pak Thighs 13#		490		Gwaltney 12-1#		578
		CANNED MEATS		491		Chunk Canadian Ends 25#		579
415		Bar-B-Q Spare Ribs 6-2½#		492		Chunk Canadian Centers 14#		580
								581

Section of order form shows typical listing of meat items identified by code.

rather than as an aid in filling orders. In comparison, data processing is an important tool in the selection of dry groceries.

In many current operations, beef quarters and lamb carcasses are moved via overhead rail to the staging area, where they are loaded on trucks. Primal cuts are generally boxed for transportation to stores.

Standard or modular orders are used by some corporate chains for their meat operations. Each store's needs are filled in accordance with a predetermined plan, with adjustments made for special promotions and in response to special requests from the store.

6. *Shipping.* A general practice is to use overhead rails in trucks that connect with the overhead rails in the distribution center so that beef quarters and lamb and veal carcasses may be pushed easily from the loading dock to the truck. Ideally, refrigerated trucks back into air seals that connect with the loading dock so that the meat is not exposed to outside air and controlled temperature is maintained.

7. *Receiving at the store.* Although the receiving function is the store's responsibility rather than the distribution center's, it is nevertheless closely related to the functions performed by the central facility.

It is highly desirable to move fresh meats from refrigerated trucks directly into store coolers in the shortest possible time, with minimum exposure to outside air. Recent progress made in the design of receiving facilities for fresh meats cannot be reflected, of course, in any but the newest or most recently remodeled stores. Air seals that connect the truck interiors to store loading docks permit the unloading of meats directly into temperature-controlled areas free from outside air. If meat receiving rails are installed at a store, they connect with the rails on the trucks.

Advantages of delivery through a distribution center

The advantages of delivery through a company's food distribution center are:

1. All the varieties of meat needed by a store may be consolidated and shipped on a single truck or trailer. The number of weekly deliveries per store can be greatly reduced, in contrast to the more than 30 required when deliveries are made directly from the packer. When shipments are concentrated into fewer deliveries, time spent in receiving at the store is reduced considerably.

2. The inspection of meats is centralized and is performed by highly skilled personnel. When a store receives meat from its own food distribution center, it has the assurance that the product has passed a rigorous quality inspection.

A central plant can afford to employ a highly qualified meat inspector, because his salary may be prorated to all the stores served by the facility. One food chain distribution director puts it this way: "We have a full-time company meat warehouse inspector who does nothing but inspect meats for grade and quality. We feel this man is very important to us and it has been through his services that we have been able to maintain the grade and quality of meats going to our stores. Our inspector is the deciding factor as to whether or not we will accept a shipment of meat or turn it down because of grade or quality."

3. Unitized shipping, which reduces costs, is possible for some items delivered to stores from distribution centers.

4. Stores receiving shipments from their own central plants have the assurance of receiving proper weight and therefore need spend much less time for weight checks than when they receive direct deliveries.

5. Store bookkeeping is reduced when deliveries are consolidated and come from a single central distribution facility.

Disadvantages of delivery through a distribution center

The disadvantages of delivery through a company's food distribution center are:

1. Shrinkage that occurs during the distribution process, as well as losses through spoilage or deterioration of product, increases the net cost of each pound. A company owns the meat it distributes through its central facility and therefore directly absorbs losses due to shrinkage, spoilage, or deterioration.

2. Large-scale buying and acceptance of deliveries at a central facility may occasionally lead to significantly overstocked conditions.

3. When delivery is made through a company's food distribution center, an investment must be made in warehouse space, equipment, trucks, and personnel.

Central meat processing

Most companies that process meats centrally limit themselves to the production of primal cuts, which must later be divided into retail cuts at the stores. Although few companies currently produce retail cuts at central plants, experts agree that centralized cutting, weighing, pricing, and packaging of retail cuts of meat, ready to be purchased by the consumer, are likely to be adopted increasingly.

Advantages of processing into primal cuts

The central production of primal cuts has the following advantages:

1. Central breaking into primal cuts involves the trimming away of waste, thus reducing the volume of weight transported to the stores. In fresh beef, for example, from 17 to 20 percent of the weight is trimmed out.[2]

[2] "The Search for a Thousand Million Dollars—Cost Reduction Opportunities in the Transportation and Distribution of Grocery Products," prepared by A. T. Kearney & Company, Inc., for the National Association of Food Chains, 1966.

2. The central production of ground beef, as a by-product of the central breaking of beef into primal cuts, can be a highly profitable and practicable operation. Plant-manufactured ground beef is produced under strict supervision and according to rigid standards. This results in a uniform, high-quality product being made available at low cost. Rough carcass trimmings, plates, and shanks may be fully utilized. Because of the advantages of assembly-line operation, ground beef may be produced more efficiently in a central plant than in individual stores.

3. A meat warehouse can produce primal cuts that are consistently uniform. For example, in breaking down a beef quarter, each loin of beef is separated from the round at the same point; carcasses of lamb and veal are processed uniformly into saddles (half a carcass) and trimmed according to standard procedures.

Although large chains use standard cutting methods in the stores, variations do occur. The cost of supervision of decentralized meat cutters, to make sure standard methods are followed, is greater, per pound of meat processed, than the cost of supervising centralized meat cutters.

In general, a central plant where meat is broken into primal cuts can be profitable if it handles sufficient capacity. According to a study by a large cooperative chain of more than 100 meat operations throughout the United States, a company-owned meat distribution center of 60,000 square feet is considered the optimum size for a large company. A plant of that size could handle 5,000,000 pounds of meat volume weekly (breaking meat into primal but not retail cuts), but would prove profitable, it is estimated, with a minimum volume of 1,000,000 pounds weekly. Assuming an average retail value of 53 cents a pound, 1,000,000 pounds would represent $530,000 of weekly retail value. At that rate of weekly production, the plant could supply about 77 supermarkets doing an average meat volume of $7,500 weekly.

Advantages of processing into retail cuts

The three advantages of central production of primal cuts discussed above are also advantages of central breaking into retail cuts. Central breaking into retail cuts has the following additional advantages:

1. The number of man-hours required to process a given quantity of product are less in a central plant than at many decentralized store locations, according to studies by a large cooperative food chain and the U.S. Department of Agriculture. Meat can be broken down more efficiently at a central plant employing assembly-line methods in which each worker performs a single function than in a store where each worker performs various functions.

The efficient operation of a store's meat department depends to a large extent on the meat manager's ability to supervise and train meat cutters to be proficient at breaking down sides and quarters, boning and trimming them, cutting the maximum profit from them, and rolling, slicing, cubing, weighing, and packaging the end product. In the judgment of many food company executives, store-level training just does not get done.

Moreover, the use of conveyors to move the meat to the cutters, specialized work stations, and other equipment at the central plant makes the work much easier than it is in the stores.

2. The ability of a meat warehouse to ship the proper cuts of meat to the stores where they are in demand is a major advantage of maintaining a central plant.

A store in a lower income area, operating under the direct store delivery system of distribution, may often have to sell T-bone, club, sirloin, and porterhouse steaks at prices lower than round steak in order to move the whole hind of beef it is obligated to order. With central processing of retail cuts, however, a store can order as many round steaks as it needs without being forced to take T-bones. Higher income areas may then be served with the beef loins.

Moreover, in territories where corned beef, for example, is in demand, a meat warehouse may pickle and package that product profitably. Where demand is specialized, the non-processed plate and brisket cuts may be sold to processors for conversion to corned beef and pastrami, and the company's stores are not burdened with cuts that are difficult to sell.

The result of such activities is that waste is reduced sharply for all stores, markdowns are controlled, and, perhaps most important, customer satisfaction is insured and customer loyalty retained by reducing out-of-stock conditions.

3. Some of the equipment used in a central plant need not be duplicated in the individual stores. High-speed wrapping machines at a central plant, for example, eliminate the need for wrapping equipment in individual stores. Moreover, central processing makes more efficient use of equipment. A central plant can use automatic scales and wrapping machinery more advantageously than can a large number of stores. Continuous runs of single cuts, such as several hundred of the same size of steak, are possible at a central plant. The machine requires only a single adjustment to show the price per pound, the weight, the net price, and the name of the cut, and to make allowance for shrinkage and the weight of the packaging material. At a store, frequent adjustments of the machine are required, since only a few dozen units of a single kind of item are packaged in any one run.

4. Equipment in use many hours a day repays the investment made

in it faster than equipment in use for only a short time each day. Highly specialized or high-volume production machines that are not economical in a retail store are well adapted to use in a central plant.

5. A food distribution center that breaks meat into retail cuts can ship its entire production in boxes. Boxed cuts can be unitized so that loading at the warehouse and unloading at the stores may be carried on more efficiently.

6. To the extent that residual trimmings, fats, and bone are marketable, a central plant can command prices ranging from 3 to 8 cents a pound, in contrast to only ¾ cent to 2 cents a pound at the store. The primary reason for the price differential is that a central plant is under Federal inspection and the fat trimmings may be disposed of as edible fats. Lack of control at the store may result in soilage of clean fats or admixture of fats and bone; trimming at a central plant, however, may be performed more efficiently. Marketing practices vary in sections of the country, however, so that warehouse trimmings have little or no value in some areas.

Disadvantages of central meat processing

The production of retail cuts of meat at a food distribution center has the following disadvantages:

1. When meat is cut, the number of surfaces exposed to air increases, thus accelerating shrinkage. To counteract this disadvantage, meat must be stored in a controlled atmosphere, a process requiring additional expense.

2. Ideally, production of retail cuts at a central plant should be balanced against demand, but that is not always possible, since a central meat processing facility must operate on an assembly-line basis. Assembly-line techniques are an advantage so far as efficient production is concerned, but a disadvantage to the extent that at certain times more product may have to be processed than can be absorbed by the stores.

3. When supply is greater than demand, an additional expense is incurred for preserving and holding the product until it is needed.

4. The sizes of portions may be too standardized and therefore individual stores may not receive package sizes they can use to the greatest advantage.

5. Temperature control from plant to stores is critically important for fresh beef and pork in retail cuts, thus entailing an expense for equipment and handling.

6. Because weight loss due to shrinkage must be allowed for, additional tolerance in weighing packages at the central plant may have to be made to assure that net weight is correct at the time of sale.

Exhibit 25. Comparative Costs for Central Meat Plant and Conventional Meat Backroom

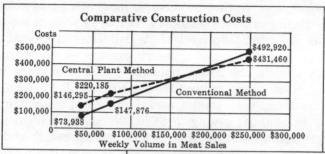

Comparative Construction Costs

- $492,920
- $431,460
- $220,185
- $146,295
- Central Plant Method
- Conventional Method
- $147,876
- $73,938

Weekly Volume in Meat Sales

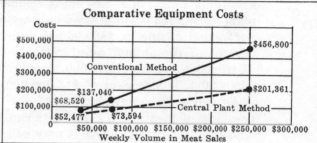

Comparative Equipment Costs

- $456,800
- Conventional Method
- $137,040
- $68,520
- $201,361
- $52,477
- $73,594
- Central Plant Method

Weekly Volume in Meat Sales

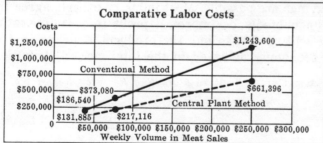

Comparative Labor Costs

- $1,243,600
- Conventional Method
- $373,080
- $186,540
- $661,396
- $131,885
- $217,116
- Central Plant Method

Weekly Volume in Meat Sales

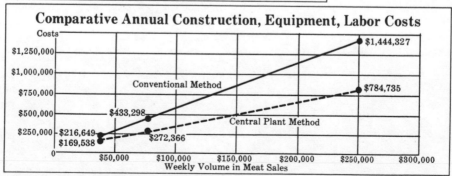

Comparative Annual Construction, Equipment, Labor Costs

- $1,444,327
- Conventional Method
- $784,735
- $433,298
- $216,649
- $169,538
- $272,366
- Central Plant Method

Weekly Volume in Meat Sales

Conventional method of processing meat in stores is compared with central plant method of producing retail cuts in a study by Agricultural Marketing Service of the U.S. Department of Agriculture (*Marketing Research Report No. 628*). Study deals with stores with $6,250 weekly volume.

In general, the cost of building and equipping a central plant for processing is lower than the total cost of building and equipping many individual store meat processing rooms. A U.S. Department of Agriculture study indicated that one central meat plant was able to achieve an annual saving of about $660,000 compared with the cost of operating under a system of direct store deliveries from packers.[3] (See Exhibit 25.) Although some industry experts do not agree with the actual data used in the study, pointing out that savings would vary with wage rates, union contracts, existing facilities, etc., they concede that the study points out a useful method of evaluating comparative costs. The annual saving of $660,000 can be achieved, the study concludes, when weekly volume is $250,000 at retail and 40 stores, averaging $6,250 in weekly meat volume, are served. The central meat plant considered in the study would occupy 12,770 square feet of space. An annual saving of $660,000 in operating cost is equal to about 5 percent of the annual retail value of the meat flowing through the distribution center ($250,000 weekly × 52 weeks = $13,000,000, and $660,000 = 5.08 percent of $13,000,000).

Although exact calculations of savings made possible by central breaking of meats into retail cuts can be determined only when specific situations are studied, it may be concluded that, in general, substantial savings are possible. Most industry experts agree that the result will undoubtedly be improved profit in meat operations, while consumers will be able to buy the products at prices that reflect the increased economies achieved in the total meat distribution process.

[3] U.S. Department of Agriculture *Marketing Research Report No. 628*, October 1963.

Glossary

Carcass—*The entire animal.*

Side (*sometimes called "straight side"*)—*Half a carcass of beef, cut from front to back, with some waste eliminated and, in some cases, with such items as kidney and brisket removed.*

Quarter—*Half a side, cut from top to bottom to yield a forequarter and a hindquarter.*

Saddle—*Half a carcass of lamb or veal, cut to yield a foresaddle (including breasts, shoulders and ribs) and a hindsaddle (including legs and loins).*

Primal cut (*sometimes called "wholesale cut"*)—*A major trimmed section. For beef, primal cuts such as round, chuck, rib and loin are taken from a side. For lamb and veal, the trimmed saddle is a primal cut. For pork, trimmed primals are identical with such large retail cuts as a full pork loin, a side of bacon, an entire ham or a side of spare ribs.*

Packer's cut—*A primal that is cut in accordance with a particular packer's method.*

Retail cut—*A prepared cut as it is sold to the retail customer.*

Boxed cuts—*Applied to beef; trimmed, boneless or bone-in primals, or retail cuts, boxed for shipment to stores.*

Block cuts—*Saw-ready cuts, either primals or sections of primals, that are larger than retail cuts.*

PRODUCE

Attractively displayed fresh produce in good variety is an important traffic and profit builder for supermarkets. According to a consumer survey, nine out of 10 shoppers buy most of their fruits and vegetables in supermarkets, in preference to other types of outlets.[1]

Basic functions in handling produce

Produce accounts for 8 to 10 percent of total supermarket sales.[2] Virtually every corporate, voluntary, and cooperative chain operates a produce warehouse as part of its food distribution center. Most of the produce sold is moved through these produce warehouses, because it is economically advantageous to purchase the commodities in large quantities for delivery to a single destination. Direct store deliveries may be made, however, for some locally produced items or for special items, such as watermelons, that can be dropped off conveniently at stores to avoid double handling during the relatively short period when they are available.

[1] 1965 Burgoyne Index, Inc., *Annual Study of Supermarket Shoppers.*
[2] *Chain Store Age.*

The proper handling of fresh produce from grower to store is a vital factor in maintaining the quality of the merchandise offered to the consumer. The food distribution center plays an important role in maintaining quality by (1) moving perishable produce quickly, (2) so handling it as to avoid bruising, and (3) providing proper levels of temperature and humidity.

Since produce costs more to warehouse and deliver, as a percentage of sales, than any other major commodity group, food companies find it worthwhile to give considerable attention to devising handling systems that best serve their particular operation.

The functions performed at a company-owned produce distribution center are listed and discussed below.

Receiving and inspection

Produce is generally received in the early morning hours. However, buyers continually check store orders against incoming merchandise and warehouse inventory and, when necessary, place orders with local suppliers for additional merchandise needed to supply stores. Thus, some local shipments may arrive as late as 8 P.M. or 9 P.M.

According to produce specialists of several leading food companies, most produce—perhaps 75 to 80 percent—is generally received by truck. Incoming merchandise is palletized by drivers. The receiving clerk pulls the product into the receiving area and dates it. Then a fork-lift truck operator moves the merchandise into the coolers. Pallets used for produce are generally a standard 48 by 40 inches.

Incoming produce is inspected as it is received. Responsibility for inspection, however, differs among various companies. In some companies, the produce warehouse superintendent is responsible for that function. In others, merchandisers or buyers inspect incoming merchandise.

Although there is little uniformity in the assignment of responsibility for inspection, all companies stress the importance of making inspections on a continual basis. Variations in quality in the natural product are inevitable, and continual alertness is required to insure adherence to a company's quality standards.

Storage

The methods used to store produce at the distribution center vary considerably from region to region and from company to company. Five basic methods are in use:

1. The produce storage space is divided into three areas—a "wet box" for items such as cabbage, carrots, celery, and corn, held at 32°F to 34°F and at 90 to 95 percent relative humidity; a "dry box" for

items such as apples, grapefruit, grapes, lemons, lettuce, oranges, and peaches, held at 32°F to 34°F and at 85 to 90 percent relative humidity; and an air-conditioned area held at 50°F to 55°F for items such as cantaloupes, tomatoes, onions, white potatoes, and sweet potatoes.

2. The produce storage space is divided into two areas—a 34°F room and a 55°F room. The 34°F room is used to hold both wet and dry perishables at 90 percent relative humidity. The 55°F room is used to hold those dry perishables requiring a higher temperature.

3. A single large area unbroken by partitions is zoned for temperature control. Cooling units are placed at various locations in the area and are set at different temperatures. Thus, the area is cooled at 55°F at one end and at 35°F to 40°F at the other, with intermediate temperatures between. A metal baffle comes down from the ceiling to about 22 feet from the floor to help separate the area into two cooling zones.

4. A single large area is maintained at a temperature ranging from 34°F to 39°F for all the merchandise.

5. If a produce distribution center is located near the area where the produce is grown so that a high percentage of items is obtained locally, or if a very fast method of moving merchandise in and out of the warehouse is employed, produce storage space may be unrefrigerated. If, in addition, stores are relatively near the distribution center and receive deliveries frequently, refrigeration at the warehouse may not be considered necessary.

Store ordering

Two basic methods are used to transmit produce orders from stores to produce distribution centers:

1. Quantities are entered on preprinted forms and sent to the distribution center, usually on the return trips of company trucks.

2. Orders are telephoned to the distribution center. Remote stores may telephone their orders to a single store in their area, after which the orders are transmitted to the produce distribution center in a single toll call. Stores call in their orders in the morning for delivery that night or early the next day. Orders are given by product code number and quantity.

In some cases, the distribution center records incoming orders on tape. The store produce manager calls the distribution center, then listens as a tape-recorded message tells him what specials are available for ordering that day, what the current prices are, and what promotions are planned. He then adjusts his order to take those facts into consideration and recites to the tape recorder the product code numbers and quantities desired.

Exhibit 26. Produce Order Form

STORE NO._____ DATE_____

	ITEM		ORDER
1	LETTUCE		
2			
3	LETTUCE RED LEAF		
4	LETTUCE BUTTER		
5	LETTUCE SALAD BOWL		
6	ROMAIN		
7			
8	ENDIVE		
9	CAULIFLOWER		
10			
11	CABBAGE		
12	CABBAGE RED		
13			
14	CARROTS		
15	CARROTS PKG.		

Simple form suffices for the ordering of produce.

All the store orders are usually entered on a form at a distribution center and a total is taken of the quantity of each item required to fill the needs of the stores. The buyers then compare that total with the quantity available in the warehouse or expected to be received that day. If necessary, they may then purchase additional produce locally for delivery later in the day. If additional merchandise is not available, they adjust the quantities to be delivered to stores in order to spread the available items fairly over the stores to be served.

Order selection

Three basic methods of order selection are in use—the conventional numeric selection, the conventional item selection and the dispersion method.

1. The conventional numeric selection system calls for items to be placed in numbered slots. The slot numbers correspond to code location numbers designated for each item. Items are usually placed on

pallets. Pallet racks are used for many items to prevent the weight of one pallet load from crushing the one beneath it.

The process of selecting produce orders is similar to that of selecting dry groceries. The selector places an empty pallet on a four-wheeler and moves from slot to slot. As he picks the ordered items, he builds his pallet load. Building a pallet load is more difficult with produce than it is with dry groceries, because of variations in the weight, density, and size of containers. Heavy items, such as lemons and oranges, are selected first, and the pallet load is topped off with lighter items. If a pallet load of produce is built up to 45 or 48 inches high, an extra pallet may be placed on top of the load to stabilize it.

2. The conventional item selection system is similar to the conventional numeric selection system, except that the selector identifies the items by name rather than by number. Both systems require flexibility in the use to which the slots are put, because of seasonal and, in some cases, daily variation in the quantities of each item received.

Some companies use conveyors on which items selected to fill a store order are moved to staging areas for loading on store delivery trucks. A conveyor system expedites an even flow of merchandise. However, it requires careful scheduling and coordination of the order-picking, staging, and loading processes, since orders must usually be selected in predetermined sequence and generally have to be picked one store at a time.

3. The dispersion method is used by some companies to move perishable produce through the distribution center in the shortest possible time and with the least number of handlings. Dry, less perishable items are usually moved into the distribution center for later handling, while highly perishable items are placed in spaces designated for each store on the unloading dock as they are unloaded from trucks and rail cars. Order assembly is substituted for the entire process of storage, selection, and subsequent order assembly. When incoming deliveries are completed, the merchandise is merged with conventionally selected, less perishable items and is immediately loaded on trucks and delivered to stores.

"In one door and out the other" is the goal of the dispersion method. Much of the inventory is rotated daily. Complete daily rotation of inventory would, however, leave no reserve stock from which to fill special store requirements. Consequently, at the buyer's direction, some portion of each shipment would be set aside in storage for special orders or for distribution the following day.

The key to effective use of the dispersion method is to be prepared to receive merchandise before it actually gets to the receiving dock. With the dispersion method, the distribution of merchandise to stores must be made on paper in advance of physical receipt of the items.

Shipping

Many companies deliver produce to stores five or six times a week, with distant stores or smaller stores receiving deliveries two or three times a week. Other companies deliver produce to all stores only two or three times a week.

Although the general practice is to use separate trucks for the delivery of produce to stores, many companies combine produce with dairy products when there is enough volume to justify use of a refrigerated truck at one set temperature.

The categories of merchandise making up mixed loads that include produce vary depending on whether the produce is to be refrigerated in transit. Thus, unrefrigerated produce may be combined with dry groceries. Refrigerated produce is more generally combined with dairy products and delicatessen or meats. If produce is combined with frozen foods, provision is made for zoned temperature compartments.

Distances from warehouse to stores as well as frequency of deliveries also affect a company's decision on refrigeration of its warehouse and its trucks. Short runs and high turnover do not require as much emphasis on refrigeration as do longer runs and lower turnover. In the latter case, of course, space requirements in the warehouse and in transit are greater and call for preserving the product for longer periods.

In the transportation of produce from warehouse to stores, the major consideration is to safeguard the products. Rough and careless handling probably contributes more than any other single factor to the deterioration of fruits and vegetables. Careful stowing of the products to be transported is of the utmost importance.

At every stage of the movement of produce precautions must be taken to avoid crushing and bruising. Any cut or bruise releases water. Cages, movable shelves, and wire-bound boxes are devices used to "containerize" the product and to firm up the loads. When a single truck delivers produce to more than one store, the driver is usually under instruction to inspect the load after each delivery and to shift items as necessary to maintain the stability of the remaining load.

Produce is usually delivered on a schedule that brings it to the stores before they open for business. One device used is a refrigerated, locked cage at the store into which night deliveries are made.

Prepackaging

The function of prepackaging produce is performed to some degree by many food distribution centers, but relatively few companies maintain large central produce prepackaging operations. Many other companies consider prepackaging to be either a store function or a grower function.

For many products, most food companies prefer produce to be pre-packaged at the grower level, because (a) it can usually be done at lower labor cost, and (b) it reduces the weight and bulk of the products to be shipped.

Certain grades of potatoes, apples, oranges, grapefruit, lettuce, cauliflower, broccoli, celery, and carrots, for example, are being prepackaged at the grower level at lower total cost than they can be prepackaged elsewhere.

Other items, for which high spoilage is a factor, such as grapes, peaches, plums, and other soft fruits, are being prepackaged successfully at store level, where quality can be carefully controlled.

Still other items, such as tomatoes, chopped salads, spinach, and bananas, are being prepackaged at company-owned distribution centers to take advantage of the possibility of quality control, mass production, and uniformity of package.

The major benefit of prepackaging produce at a company-owned distribution center is that it insures control of quality. Quality control hinges on buying, inspecting, and handling procedures that yield the finest products. There is general agreement that a produce prepackaging program stands or falls on the degree to which high quality of product is maintained.

Since one out of every three supermarkets sells virtually all its fresh fruits and vegetables in prepackaged form and since almost all supermarkets sell some prepackaged produce items,[3] the question of where and how produce is prepackaged is of continuing interest to store operators and produce buyers.

Banana ripening

With the availability of bananas ripened by suppliers, some companies have planned future distribution centers without banana ripening facilities. Other companies, however, plan to build banana ripening rooms in future distribution centers.

Control of quality is the principal advantage cited by several food companies to justify the operation of their own banana ripening facilities. The purpose of maintaining such facilities is to assure a supply of good quality, ripened bananas to fill store needs as they arise.

In areas where several suppliers provide bananas, a company can "fill in" if its major supplier cannot deliver the right product at the right time, and a company-operated banana ripening facility may not be required. In areas where the availability of supply is limited, a company-operated banana ripening facility can bring the green bananas to the ripe stage at controlled rates of speed timed to coincide

[3] *The Supermarket Industry Speaks—1966,* Super Market Institute, Chicago.

with demand, thus reducing dependence on a single supplier.

Banana ripening is a special process that requires special equipment. A typical ripening procedure is to check bananas as they are unloaded and to determine if they are ready for ripening. If so, they are held for 24 hours at 68°F to 70°F; then steam is applied at 20-minute intervals. When the temperature of the fruit has dropped to 60°F to 65°F, it is held for color observation. When the color is judged to be right, the temperature is dropped a bit and the bananas are held until they are ready to be cut from their stems. The ripening process generally takes between 36 and 48 hours, depending on the fruit itself and on the necessity for hastening or slowing the process in relation to demand. Boxed bananas, already cut from their stems, are now available in both green and ripe condition.

The gas-tight rooms in which bananas are ripened may also be used for other purposes. An innovation that produce specialists believe will be practical is to purchase strawberries as they become available and hold them in a gas-tight room into which nitrogen is injected. The nitrogen blankets the product and keeps oxygen away from it. The gas also holds the product at the temperature at which it was placed in the room. Strawberries may be held in storage for a limited time in nitrogen and shipped to stores to meet demand. Some leafy vegetables such as lettuce may also be held in nitrogen-filled rooms. However, the use of nitrogen in the storage of produce has not had as widespread recognition as has the use of that gas in the shipping of produce for long distances.

Estimating space needs

Space requirements for a produce warehouse obviously vary with the functions to be performed at the warehouse. Factors that affect the total space needed include:

1. Whether space must be provided for refrigeration equipment.
2. The method of handling (dispersion versus selection line).
3. The amount of prepackaging performed.
4. Whether bananas will be ripened.
5. How high pallets will be stacked in the racks.
6. Frequency of delivery.
7. Rate of turnover.

In general, produce requires much less space per ton moved per year than does dry groceries. This is due primarily to the much higher rate of turnover for fresh produce than can be realized in dry groceries. Total produce inventory turns over about twice every week. Some estimates of space requirements are: 40 to 60 square feet per ton of average inventory, based on an average on one-half week's supply of produce plus one and three-quarters weeks' supply of bananas; 22,000 square feet to handle 1,000 tons of produce per week, using drive-in racks with an 18-foot-high ceiling; 25,000 square feet to handle weekly 350 tons of dairy and produce combined, including excess capacity for expansion.[4]

As these ratios indicate, no one formula is available to cover all situations. The seven factors that affect the total space needed must be studied in detail before a produce distribution center is constructed.

[4] *NAFC Management Clinic Reports.*

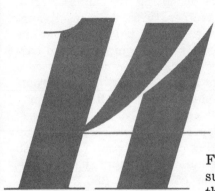

FROZEN FOODS

Frozen foods account for at least 5 percent of total supermarket volume. In many individual stores, they make up somewhat more than that proportion of total sales. Hence, the volume of merchandise handled per store is great enough for a warehouse to be economically justified even when it is to serve a comparatively small number of stores.

A volume as low as 30 to 40 tons of frozen foods weekly is sufficient to make it feasible for a company to consider warehousing frozen foods. The alternative method of distribution is through wholesalers. A company operates its own frozen foods warehouse when it can perform the distribution functions more efficiently than can a wholesaler.

Frozen foods distribution

The frozen foods distribution process consists of receiving, storing, order selection, shipping, and receiving at the store. All these activities are performed under controlled temperature conditions.

The chief enemy of frozen foods is heat. Although the truth of that statement may seem obvious, careful analysis of the steps required to maintain frozen foods at the proper temperature indicates that many individuals who perform key jobs in moving the merchandise from supplier to consumer have not yet understood that single, basic fact.

Thus, food retailers, in addition to supplying warehouse buildings, freezers, transportation equipment, receiving freezers, and carefully engineered display cases for frozen foods, must maintain constant vigilance to make sure the product is handled at the proper temperature at every step of the distribution process.

Receiving and storage

Frozen foods must be kept at temperatures of 0°F or below—down to −5°F to −15°F. In the late 1950s inbound receipts via truck carriers were reaching receiving docks at temperatures in excess of 10°F above zero, and in some cases rejections were running as high as 30 percent. Investigation revealed that some carriers' equipment could not maintain the proper temperatures and had to be repaired or replaced, and that some carriers were accepting merchandise from storage warehouses at excessively high temperatures. As a result, suppliers were notified that shipments in excess of 0°F would not be accepted. Vendors were asked to inspect carriers' equipment and carriers were asked to make temperature checks when products were tendered for shipment. Purchase orders began to carry specific routing instructions to be followed by vendors. As a result of the program, rejections of shipments were reduced sharply.

One way in which retailers are cooperating with carriers is by scheduling delivery times and organizing the receiving function so that redeliveries are reduced to a minimum. Recognizing that maintenance of a refrigerated truck and driver costs about $80 a day, retailers make every effort to accept merchandise when it arrives.

Today, inbound receipts are not a major problem, but continual checking is necessary to insure adherence to standards. Except for frozen fruit juices, cauliflower, green beans, and asparagus, frozen produce does not show damage until the temperature of the product gets above 18°F to 20°F, at which point visual inspection reveals the damage. Nevertheless, real damage is done to frozen products when they are stored at 5°F to 15°F, the damage due primarily to a loss of vitamin C content.[1]

Frozen products held at 33°F for three hours have a three-degree rise in temperature. Each additional hour contributes an additional rise of one degree when the product is held in whole cases. Consequently, every effort is made to move the product from the receiving area into the storage area as fast as possible. The best practice, of course, is to maintain the receiving area at a low temperature, using seals between trucks and receiving dock.

[1] "Frozen Food Problems," by H. M. Thornton, Colonial Stores, Inc., *N.A.F.C. Management Clinic Report*, May 1954.

Exhibit 27. Frozen Foods Order Form

FROZEN FOOD
PRICE - ORDER GUIDE

All advertised items are to be stocked and sold at advertised prices.
All price changes during week are to be entered on this sheet immediately.
Prices must be changed in the retail area immediately.

COMMODITY PRICE	CODE	OPENING INVENTORY	ORDERING RECORD FOR DELIVERY					TOTAL	CLOSING INVENTORY	SALES
PREPARED FOODS			TUE	WED	THU	FRI	SAT			
ROMAN CHEESE RAVIOLA 12/12 Oz. 2/99¢	400									
ROMAN MANICOTTI 12/12 Oz. 55¢	401									
ROMAN PARTY PIZZA 12/15 Oz. 65¢	402									
BUITONI LASAGNE 12/14 Oz. 59¢	404									
CURLY'S PIEROGIES 12/6's 2/79¢	405									
MORTON Macaroni & Cheese 24/8 Oz. 2/39¢	407									
Mrs. Paul's Fr. Fried Onion Rings 12/5 Oz. 2/59¢	410									
Mrs. Paul's Fr. Fried Onion Rings 12/9 oz. 2/99¢	411									
Mrs. Paul's Candied Swt. Potatoes 12/12 Oz. 3/$1.00	413									
MRS. PAUL'S APPLE FRITTERS 12/8 Oz. 2/79¢	414									
MRS PAUL'S CORN FRITTERS 12/7 Oz. 2/79¢	415									
STOUFFER Macaroni & Cheese 12/12 Oz. 2/85¢	421									
STOUFFER Potatoes Au Gratin 12/11½ Oz. 2/95¢	422									
STOUFFER WELSH RAREBIT 12/10 Oz. 65¢	423									
STOUFFERS MAC. & BEEF 12/11½Oz. 65¢	424									
STOUFFERS SPINACH SOUFFLE 12/12 Oz. 2/95¢	425									
STOUFFER CAULIF. AU Gratin 12/10 Oz. 2/99¢	426									
STOUFFERS BROC. AU GRATIN 12/10 Oz. 2/99¢	427									
DORANN BAKED POT. 12/19 Oz. 2/89¢	428									
OH BOY POTATOES w/CHIVES 12/12 Oz. 2/79¢	429									
DORANN FOLY POTATO PUFFS	431									

Space is provided for ordering record throughout week.

Store ordering

Three basic methods are used by stores to order frozen foods from company-owned distribution centers:

1. If produce orders are telephoned in to the distribution center, it is relatively simple for the store to add its frozen food requirements to a telephoned produce order.

2. Conventional order forms, with each frozen food item listed by name and code number, are filled in and mailed to the warehouse or delivered to the warehouse by company trucks on their return trips. Store order forms are generally revised every four weeks to include new items, eliminate slow movers, and take seasonal factors into account.

3. Mark-sense cards are supplied to stores. The cards are marked with a graphite pencil to indicate, in code, the items and quantities desired. At the distribution center, the cards are converted to conventional punched cards, from which a selection list is printed.

Order selection

Most companies select frozen foods from standard grocery-type pallet racks and place them on pallets, semi-live skids, or platform trucks. One type of fork-lift truck permits the operator to select items from the racks while he stands on a raised pallet; this procedure extends the effective capacity of the selection line by using the full height of the cooler or freezer.

Other methods used include:

1. *Conveyors.* Many companies use conveyors to assist in the selection of orders. To take advantage of the continuous flow of the conveyor and to utilize costly cubic space, a number of installations provide for two levels of inventory along the selection line.

An order filler selects items along the lower level and places them on a conveyor that parallels the selection line. He then climbs to a catwalk and fills orders from the upper level of inventory, placing the items on another conveyor that runs above the first.

If an operation is big enough (80,000 to 100,000 square feet) to warrant it, the upper level of inventory may duplicate the lower level of stock. In that way, selectors may feed both the upper and the lower conveyors simultaneously with orders. This method provides for greater flexibility than the one in which the two levels contain unduplicated inventory.

Another system calls for four parallel rows of racks with a conveyor running between each of two rows. The parallel conveyors join and feed a telescoping conveyor that is projected into a truck. Four men make selections and two men load, and the crew can fill a 32-foot

Exhibit 28. Conveyor Lines Merge

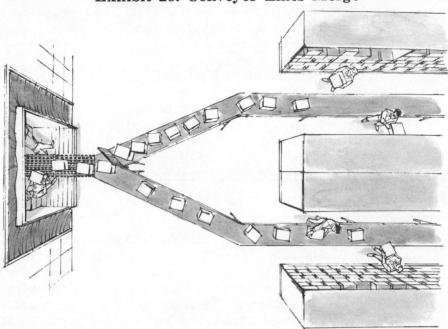

One system of order filling for frozen foods allows four men to select merchandise for a single store, which they place on conveyor lines. The conveyors meet and the store order flows into a truck over another conveyor that telescopes so that it may be drawn out of the truck as the vehicle is being loaded.

trailer in one hour. The system is reported to work well for a warehouse with from 300 to 500 tons of weekly shipments where loading only one truck at a time is satisfactory. (Exhibit 28.)

2. *Pallet-flow racks.* Another method of selection of frozen foods makes use of a pallet-flow rack system. Pallet loads of merchandise are placed into racks from the rear, the pallets roll forward to the selection aisle, and the selector picks items from the front.

Many variations of this system are in use. One company, for example, uses its racks in conjunction with a double-decked conveyor system. The second-level conveyor is 7½ feet above the floor. The selector uses a catwalk to reach merchandise intended for the upper-level conveyor.

Selected merchandise is carried on the conveyors to a central point, where it is counted and weighed automatically. Production is at the rate of about 450 cases an hour.

Several companies that used standard pallets in slots from which frozen foods were selected (similar to a dry groceries selection line) have replaced them with pallet-flow racks. With the changeover to pallet-flow racks, increases ranging from 20 to 50 percent were reported in the effective utilization of warehouse space.

Order assembling

The staging area, where merchandise is held prior to being loaded on trucks should also, ideally, be a low-temperature area. If this is not possible, then emphasis must be placed on speed in moving the product into refrigerated trucks. In smaller operations, it is often feasible to convey store orders directly into waiting trucks as the items are selected. Larger operations usually require an intermediate step, in which the merchandise is held in the staging area prior to loading.

Transportation to stores

Many companies deliver frozen foods to stores twice or three times weekly. To obtain economical loads, several store orders are placed on each truck. As the truck door is opened at each stop, heat is added to the load whenever the outside temperature is higher than the temperature inside the truck. Therefore, in hot weather, unloading must be accomplished quickly and the merchandise moved speedily to a temperature-controlled environment.

If a shipment consists entirely of frozen foods, it is usually held at 0°F. If frozen foods are combined with ice cream, a temperature of −10°F is maintained. If ice cream and frozen foods are delivered at the same time, priority in unloading is usually given to ice cream. According to one warehouse director, combining ice cream and frozen foods on trucks is the key to successful, efficient operation of a frozen foods warehouse (see Exhibit 29 below).

Mechanical refrigeration is customarily used in transporting frozen foods, although experiments are being conducted involving injection of "shots" of liquid nitrogen after each delivery stop, to maintain the truck at a low temperature.

Frozen foods may also be transported in insulated containers; however, the containers occupy additional space and add considerably to total weight.

One method used to prevent warm air from entering a refrigerated truck calls for the driver to feed a store order from inside the truck on to a conveyor, which leaves the truck through a 30-by-30-inch opening. The opening has a flap of canvas or nylon over it; the flap is pushed outward by the merchandise as it moves out of the truck on the conveyor, but it covers the opening when no merchandise is moving out.

The possibility of frozen foods being damaged by heat transmission

Exhibit 29. Combination Loads of Ice Cream and Frozen Foods

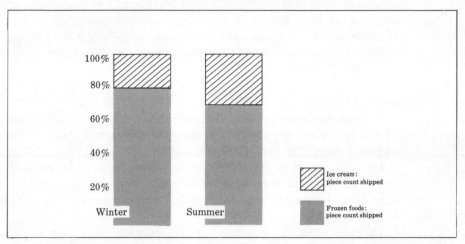

The number of pieces shipped to meet store needs in the winter permits a truck load to be made up containing 80 percent frozen foods and 20 percent ice cream. In the summer, frozen foods decrease to 70 percent as ice cream rises to 30 percent. Shipping frozen foods and ice cream together can thus be economical.

increases in proportion to the number of stops that a truck will make. A truck generally averages eight stops per trip in delivering a straight load of frozen foods. If the distances between stores are relatively short, heat entering the truck during frequent opening and closing of doors may be combated by (a) loading the product at a very low temperature at the warehouse; (b) preventing air-temperature rise in the truck by using sliding rather than hinged doors (hinged doors in many situations cannot be closed until a truck pulls away from a dock); (c) paying special attention to truck insulation; and (d) maintaining cooling units on trucks in top operating condition.

Typical deliveries

A typical frozen foods delivery in a 30-foot-long trailer contains 18 pallet loads of 70 cases each, or a total of 1,260 cases. At about 20 pounds per case, a load weighs 25,200 pounds, plus the weight of the pallets. Eighteen pallets at 54 pounds each bring the total pallet weight to 972 pounds. If a pallet jack is carried on the truck to service smaller stores, another 350 pounds is added to the weight of the load. Thus, a total load of about 26,500 pounds is typical.

There are several methods used to compute transportation costs. One of the generally accepted methods used is based on 90 cents per mile for frozen foods; another is based on 42 cents per hundredweight as the average cost.

Dispatchers calculate that every 100 miles traveled requires an average of four hours. Truck stops for frozen foods deliveries may vary from 12 to 40 minutes per stop, depending on the size of the order, the number of persons unloading, and the method used to unload and check the order.

Frequency of deliveries

Frozen foods warehouse inventories generally contain an average of three weeks' supply, but some companies maintain from one and one-half weeks' to two weeks' supply.

Drawing on that inventory, stores generally order once or twice a week, although a few companies that rely on once-a-week ordering split their deliveries into two or three parts for shipment throughout a week.

In general, a store requiring 350 cases or less per week—making up five pallet loads or less—may easily be serviced on a once-a-week basis. Stores requiring more than 350 cases a week generally receive two or more deliveries weekly. The freezer capacity of a store limits the amount of frozen foods it can receive in a single delivery.

Frequency of delivery and the practicable number of cases delivered per store vary also with the distance of the store from the warehouse. In the relatively few cases in which stores are located about 150 miles from the distribution center, money spent to add frozen food storage space at the stores is quickly recouped by savings made by reducing the number of deliveries required per year.

Obviously, if stores have abundant storage space, warehouse space and inventory may be reduced. If they have limited storage space, warehouse space and inventory must be greater.

The trend is toward smaller storage areas in the stores, except for those quite distant from a warehouse. By shortening the lead time between ordering and delivery or by delivering more frequently, store storage areas can be reduced materially.

Some companies deliver frozen foods from their own distribution centers to all stores except those too far from the center for economical truck runs. In those cases, frozen foods are delivered by outside suppliers who may be able to combine loads for the stores of several companies and thus achieve economical runs.

Receiving at the store

Because frozen foods must be maintained under controlled conditions during every step of the distribution process, proper temperature control at stores is a vital part of that distribution process.

When frozen foods are delivered, store personnel must be ready to receive the shipment the moment it arrives, and merchandise must be moved to a temperature-controlled environment as quickly as possible.

Once the product is in the store, the stock must be rotated (most companies date the product at the warehouse), and the merchandise must never be stacked above the danger line in a display case.

Warehouse costs

A frozen foods warehouse costs about $20 per square foot to build, exclusive of land. Conveyors, racks, and fork lifts can easily add another $20 per square foot to the cost of the installation. These estimates are for installations that do not include automated equipment. Thus, the capital investment for a 40,000-square-foot conventional facility, exclusive of land, would be $1,600,000.

A conventionally operated 40,000-square-foot warehouse would ship about 45,000 cases of frozen foods weekly, at the rate of 100 cases per hour (including fork-lift operation, selection, and loading). One shift would receive merchandise; another would ship it. Thus, two supervisory executives, as well as crews, would be required to perform a total of 450 man-hours of work weekly. At an estimated cost per man-hour (including all fringe benefits) of $4, the weekly payroll for the crews would be $1,800. At $200 a week each, two supervisory executives would cost $400 a week. Maintenance and sanitation personnel (two men at $150 a week each) would cost $300 a week. Total payroll would thus be $2,500 a week.

The 45,000 cases shipped weekly would have an estimated retail value of $5 a case, or a total of $225,000. Warehouse payroll would thus be 1 percent of the retail value of merchandise shipped.

Although transportation costs may vary widely, an estimate of 80 percent of warehousing operations cost is considered reasonable, or 0.8 percent of the retail value of merchandise shipped.

Depreciation of the building (on a 10-year basis) and of the fixtures (on a 7-year basis), plus interest, utilities, taxes, pallet replacement, and security personnel would increase costs about 1 percent of the retail value of merchandise shipped.

Total operating cost would therefore be 2.8 percent of retail value shipped. This figure compares with 2 to 2.5 percent for dry groceries. All of the above computations are based on figures reported to NAFC Warehousing and Transportation Clinics.

Space requirements

One way to calculate total space requirements for the warehousing of frozen foods is to allow one square foot of space for every $21.50

worth (at cost) of inventory that is held in the distribution center.

Another way is to allow 2½ cubic feet of space per case, when 300 items are carried in inventory. When 400 items are carried, 3 cubic feet of space are allocated per case as more aisle space is needed when the number of facings is increased. This calculation assumes that 85 percent of the total area will be rack storage and 15 percent bulk storage. As the percentage of bulk storage space increases, the cubic footage required per case decreases, since proportionately less aisle space is needed and cases may be stacked higher in bulk storage areas.

The future: automated warehousing

Although only a handful of automated frozen foods warehouses are in operation today, many companies are likely to automate such warehouses in the future.

Frozen foods lend themselves to automated warehousing more than any other line of foods.

Most standard frozen products are packed in containers of uniform size. Uniformity of size and a limited range of weights per cubic foot expedite handling by mechanical means.

Each packing unit of frozen foods is light enough (20 to 25 pounds) to be carried with ease on a moving belt or other type of conveyor. Automated handling is simplified when continuous conveyor operation is possible.

Frozen foods are stored and selected in the 0°F to −15°F range. Because it is undesirable to have employees working under these low-temperature conditions, many companies are searching for acceptable ways of using mechanized means to perform these functions.

Machinery is more adaptable than man power to operation in low temperatures. Men require special clothing and relatively frequent rest periods if they are to operate at top efficiency in very cold environments. Difficult working conditions resulting in high labor costs per unit of output make automation particularly attractive in handling frozen foods. Thus, the incentive to find satisfactory automated methods is greater in the handling of frozen foods than in the handling of many other products.

Frozen foods lend themselves to automation because relatively few individual items must be handled. From 300 to 400 items cover the needs of most frozen foods operations, although upwards of 750 additional items are available.

It is relatively easy to combine automated operations with some manual handling of frozen foods. Parts of the warehousing process may be automated and, on the basis of experience, additional mechanization may be installed as it appears to be justified.

Many partially automated frozen foods warehouses are in operation. In the opinions of several industry authorities, the point at which extensive automated handling may be considered is reached when about 400 tons are shipped weekly to serve approximately 100 stores. Many other companies, however, feel that the judicious application of simple equipment such as racks, pallets, conveyors, and fork-lift trucks can speed handling and decrease costs without the need to install a "push-button warehouse."

Automation concepts

Applications of the automation concept for frozen foods usually require the use of conveyor belts or monorail-type conveyors.

When one store's order must be completely selected before another's can be moved through on a conveyor, the capacity of a warehouse to expand its production is necessarily limited.

One system that overcomes the problem of limited selection makes use of identifying colored crayon marks placed on each case selected for a specific store. An order filler marks each case with a special crayon and places the case in a tray with a slotted bottom. The tray is attached to a monorail-type conveyor. As the tray containing the case of merchandise passes over a sensing-eye unit, switches are activated so that the case is shunted into a chute leading to an area designated to hold the items selected for a specific store. The use of four identifying colors permits order selection for four stores to be made simultaneously by four order fillers. Thus, four trucks may be loaded at a time. By the addition of coded colors and chutes, several additional sorts may easily be provided.

The concept of automation in such an installation has been applied to the sorting of items for specific stores after the items themselves have been selected manually.

A system that automates the selection process starts with store orders recorded on punched cards. The cards are fed into a device that activates magnetic switches which, in turn, open gates along the selection line. Behind each gate is a specific product on a "slide"—an inclined shelf. When a gate opens, a unit of the product is released, and slides on to a moving conveyor belt. When all the punched cards representing a single store's frozen foods order have been run through the device, all the items required to fill that order have been released to the conveyor and moved to a temporary storage, or surge, line, where they are held for loading. A variation of this system can bring the main conveyor line directly into an empty truck or trailer; however, a surge line is generally required as it is necessary to mark time to compensate for the difference in speed between fast order filling and slower manual loading of trucks.

Another automated operation stocks 350 frozen food items at −10°F and ships from 15,000 to 25,000 cases a day, with 70 percent of tonnage handled through automation. A total of 200 roller chutes is used in the system. Two trucks are loaded simultaneously, but the system may readily be adapted to the simultaneous loading of six trucks. Selection is made at the rate of 2,500 cases per hour or more than 40 cases per minute.

An experimental idea, under consideration by several companies, calls for elimination of a store order form or picking sheet as a guide for the order filler. The store order is placed on punched cards, which are inserted in a special device. As a result, small signs are lighted, each sign designating the quantity to be selected of the item stored under the sign. The order filler proceeds down the selection line. Whenever he sees a lighted sign, he selects the designated quantity of the indicated item and places it on a conveyor that parallels the selection line. Thus, the order filler, simply by following the directions given him by the lighted signs, may work with both hands free.

Although this system is still highly experimental, and may or may not prove to be effective in reducing costs or speeding selection, it has already demonstrated its effectiveness in accurate selection. The system is an interesting indication of the time and effort that are going into attempts to apply concepts of mechanization to the frozen foods warehousing task.

Although the term "automation" is correctly applied to an automatic system, it should nevertheless be noted that the positioning of the items behind the proper gates is necessarily an operation that must be performed by man power. Incoming merchandise, whether handled on pallets by fork-lift trucks or pallet jacks, or stacked case by case in the proper slots, must in all cases be identified by a warehouse employee and placed by him in the correct position. Only then can the automatic system take over the operation.

Advances in food preservation

The technology of food preservation is continually making strides leading to new directions. Frozen dehydrated products coming into the market may require changes in freezer facilities in the future. On the other hand, the irradiation of food, a new method of preservation without freezing, may make some freezer facilities unnecessary in the future.

As new types of frozen foods are developed, produced and promoted, however, consumer demand for them will undoubtedly increase, so that facilities for handling and selling frozen foods may have to be augmented.

Whatever changes may come, industry experts agree that frozen foods will undoubtedly continue to make important contributions to supermarket sales and profits for many years to come and that efficiency in handling them will continue to be vital.

DAIRY, DELICATESSEN, AND BAKED GOODS

Dairy items are handled at a food distribution center in much the same fashion as dry groceries, except that dairy products are stored, selected, and shipped under refrigeration. Because of the many small items and the variety of shapes and sizes of containers that make up a typical dairy order, however, it is somewhat more difficult to handle dairy products than dry groceries.

Handling dairy products

The basic functions of receiving, storing, order selecting, and shipping of dairy products are handled at a food distribution center as follows:

1. *Receiving.* Dairy products are received daily. Some items, such as eggs and high-volume cheeses, may be received on pallets, but

most items are shipped unpalletized. When they are received, they are placed on pallets on the receiving dock and hauled to storage areas by fork-lift trucks. Because many small items must be handled, morning deliveries are preferred at the distribution center to allow sufficient time for palletizing.

2. *Storage.* Dairy products are stored under 32°F to 34°F refrigeration. Most dairy products are stored on pallets, which in turn are placed on pallet racks so that order selectors will have access to more than one facing at each location. Since most dairy products are packaged in cases that are smaller than typical dry groceries cases,

Exhibit 30. Dairy Order Form

DAIRY ORDER

LINE NO.	QUANT ORDER	SIZE	DESCRIPTION	CASE PACK	UNIT RETAIL	LINE NO.	QUANT ORDER	SIZE	DESCRIPTION	CASE PACK	UNIT RETAIL
			KRAFT						**BORDENS**		
195		8 oz	AMER NAT SL SHP	12		293		8 oz	AMERICAN SLICED	12	
						294		8 oz	WHITE AMER SL	12	
197		8 oz	AM DELUXE WH SL	12							
198		8 oz	AM DELUXE COL SL	12		296		1½#	SLICED AMER	12	
199		8 oz	MUENSTER DELUXE	12		297		4 oz	CAMEMBERT	12	
200		8 oz	OLD ENG DELUXE	12		298		4 oz	LIEDERKRANTZ	12	
						299		3 oz	CHIVE	12	
						300		3 oz	PIMENTO	12	
203		8 oz	SWISS DOM SL	24		301		8 oz	NEUFSCHATEL	12	
						302		3 oz	NEUFSCHATEL	12	
205		8 oz	CREAM CH PHILA	12		303		6 oz	BLUE BARS	12	
206		3 oz	CREAM CH PHILA	12		304		6 oz	BAR CHIVES	12	
207		3 oz	CR CH PHILA-CHIVE	12		305		6 oz	CLAM & LOB BARS	12	
208		3 oz	CR CH PHILA-PIM	12		306		6 oz	BARS DATE & NUT	12	
						307		6 oz	BARS PIMENTO	12	
210		1#	CHEESE WHIZ	12		308		4 oz	GRATED AMERICAN	12	
211		8 oz	CHEESE WHIZ	12		309		2 oz	GRATED AMERICAN	12	
						310		3 oz	GRATED ITALIAN	12	
213		8 oz	CRACK BAR SH	24		311		1½oz	GRATED ITALIAN	12	
214		8 oz	CRACK BAR EX SH	24		312		5 oz	JAR BLUE	12	
215		10oz	CRACK BAR MEL ST	12		313		5 oz	JAR CH & BACON	12	
216		10oz	CRACK BAR SH ST	12		314		5 oz	JAR VERA SHARP	12	
217		10oz	CRACK BAR EX SH ST	12		315		5 oz	JAR LIMBURGER	12	

Items are identified by name and line number on simple dairy order form.

many more cases may be stacked on a pallet.

3. *Order selection.* Each dairy item is usually listed on the order form by code number, name, size, and quantity packed per case. Items are generally stored along the distribution center selection line in the same sequence as they are listed on the store order. Since only about 500 items are handled in a typical dairy department (including delicatessen and refrigerated fish items), few companies find it necessary to convert the store order listing sequence into the warehouse location sequence.

The selection procedure calls for an order selector pushing a four-wheeler along the selection line to build a pallet load of items as he moves along a predetermined path. Because dairy products are packed in relatively small cases and in containers of varied sizes, the process of building a pallet load is somewhat more time-consuming than it is for dry groceries.

4. *Shipping.* Completed orders of dairy products are generally merged with completed orders of produce and shipped in the same trucks with produce, as they can be held in the same temperature range. Dairy products may be shipped on pallets or in hand-stacked fashion.

Generally, shipment of dairy products from a company warehouse to stores is made three times a week for larger stores and two times a week for smaller stores. At the same time, each supermarket gets an average of 18 additional deliveries a week from various vendors of dairy products in the area.[1]

Central processing

Many companies cut, slice, and wrap a number of varieties of cheese and delicatessen items at their food distribution centers. These companies consider central processing of bulk cheese into resale units to be efficient and economical; furthermore, they believe that it has additional benefits, such as quality control, product identification to enhance a company's image in the cheese department, and increased sales.

The same benefits apply to the slicing and wrapping of luncheon meats at a food distribution center. In addition, consolidation of store deliveries is possible when dairy and delicatessen operations are centrally combined. A reduction in the number of deliveries that must

[1] "Warehousing Frozen Foods and Dairy," by Rodney L. Renne, The Grand Union Company, *NAFC Summary Report*, Management Clinic on Warehousing and Transportation, March 1965.

Exhibit 31. Simplified Item Coding

Please Post on Your Dairy Box

DAY OF YEAR

Day of Month	Jan	Feb	Mar	Apr	May	Jun	Jul	Aug	Sep	Oct	Nov	Dec
1	1	32	60	91	121	152	182	213	244	274	305	335
2	2	33	61	92	122	153	183	214	245	275	306	336
3	3	34	62	93	123	154	184	215	246	276	307	337
4	4	35	63	94	124	155	185	216	247	277	308	338
5	5	36	64	95	125	156	186	217	248	278	309	339
6	6	37	65	96	126	157	187	218	249	279	310	340
7	7	38	66	97	127	158	188	219	250	280	311	341
8	8	39	67	98	128	159	189	220	251	281	312	342
9	9	40	68	99	129	160	190	221	252	282	313	343
10	10	41	69	100	130	161	191	222	253	283	314	344
11	11	42	70	101	131	162	192	223	254	284	315	345
12	12	43	71	102	132	163	193	224	255	285	316	346
13	13	44	72	103	133	164	194	225	256	286	317	347
14	14	45	73	104	134	165	195	226	257	287	318	348
15	15	46	74	105	135	166	196	227	258	288	319	349
16	16	47	75	106	136	167	197	228	259	289	320	350
17	17	48	76	107	137	168	198	229	260	290	321	351
18	18	49	77	108	138	169	199	230	261	291	322	352
19	19	50	78	109	139	170	200	231	262	292	323	353
20	20	51	79	110	140	171	201	232	263	293	324	354
21	21	52	80	111	141	172	202	233	264	294	325	355
22	22	53	81	112	142	173	203	234	265	295	326	356
23	23	54	82	113	143	174	204	235	266	296	327	357
24	24	55	83	114	144	175	205	236	267	297	328	358
25	25	56	84	115	145	176	206	237	268	298	329	359
26	26	57	85	116	146	177	207	238	269	299	330	360
27	27	58	86	117	147	178	208	239	270	300	331	361
28	28	59	87	118	148	179	209	240	271	301	332	362
29	29	59a*	88	119	149	180	210	241	272	302	333	363
30	30		89	120	150	181	211	242	273	303	334	364
31	31		90		151		212	243		304		365

*Leap year.

To find the meaning of a code number, refer to heading of vertical column for the month and refer to number in the first column on the same line for the day of that month. Thus, 130 means May 10.

be received weekly by each store means a reduction in store labor expense.

Delicatessen

Many companies combine a central cheese slicing and wrapping operation with a delicatessen operation, since a number of the procedures in both departments may be performed by interchangeable personnel and under the same conditions of temperature and humidity.

Delicatessen operations can range all the way from simple slicing and wrapping of luncheon meats to the preparation and packaging of a variety of salads and regional specialties such as frozen enchiladas, pot pies, and barbecued poultry and beef.

Shelf life of prepared salads varies with the product. The manager of a highly successful central delicatessen operation advises store personnel to order salads "very close—the trick is to be out of stock when the next order comes in."

In the salad kitchen of this food chain's plant, sliced cheeses and meats, salads, and other prepared products are coded to indicate when they were processed. Two items, taken at random from each production run, are kept in a home refrigerator and checked to determine whether the production process, especially the heat-sealing of packages, is proceeding normally.

This company's key to its delicatessen operation is flexibility. A test kitchen is maintained where the company's home economist prepares lunches from the department's products and serves them to buyers as well as to panels of customers. Ideas for new products—particularly salads—are generated at the luncheons, and the company promptly tries them out in a few stores.

As a result of such experiments, twelve different kinds of gelatin salads, for example, were developed, thus giving the company a variety of offerings that led to high delicatessen department sales per store.

If a central facility is set up to slice and wrap both luncheon meats and cheese, and to make salads, a weekly volume of $15,000 to $20,000 in those items is reported by some companies to be sufficient to justify operating the facility.

Extensive supermarket delicatessen departments are on the increase. Some 46 percent of the supermarkets in operation have departments that are "extensive" in the judgment of the companies responding to an SMI survey, and half of them are supplied from central plants where delicatessen items are prepared.[2]

[2] *The Super Market Industry Speaks—1966*, Super Market Institute, Chicago.

Central cheese packaging

Some companies have moved extensively into central cheese packaging. Analysis of the following factors assists a distribution center to determine whether to embark on a central cheese processing program:

1. *Cheese market.* Analysis of trends in the cost of cheese, including the cost of various cheeses in bulk compared with the cost in packaged, delivered form.

2. *Cheese sales trends.* Study of national, regional, competitive, and company sales volume, with company projections based on (a) continuation of old buying practices and (b) establishing a packaged cheese facility.

3. *Packaging methods.* A review of all available reports on the latest techniques, supplemented by an analysis of first hand observations of plants engaged in cheese packaging.

4. *Packaging operations.* Descriptions of steps to be taken to insure production of high quality products, and costs of labor, packaging equipment and materials required.

5. *Storage conditions.* Analysis of space requirements in stores and in central plant.

6. *Waste and shrink.* Analysis of cost of shrink in aging, and of waste in slicing bulk cheese and in packaging chunks.

7. *Production capacity.* Estimates of minimum production required for economic viability; and estimated maximum capacity of a projected plant, without expansion of facilities.

8. *Inventory requirements.* Estimates of average investment required for cheese held in storage, cheese being processed, and cheese ready for sale at the store.

9. *Delivery and store-receiving costs.* Comparison of number of store deliveries required from vendors and from central plant.

10. *Land and building costs.* Evaluation of several locations in terms of relative cost. A number of building plans may also be considered.

11. *Alternatives.* Evaluating various plans and estimating the investment for each. (An operation confined to the packaging of chunk cheese, for example, requires about one half the investment in equipment that an operation engaged in the packaging of sliced cheese does.)

Every effort is made to reduce each factor to a dollars-and-cents basis, so that the final decision may be based on investment required and expected return on that investment. It should be noted, however, that some factors, such as quality of product, company image, morale of personnel, and promotional advantages cannot be reduced to an exact dollars-and-cents basis. Those factors, nevertheless, must be taken into account and, in borderline situations, may be decisive in determining the course of action to be taken.

Operating fluid milk plants

Is it more advantageous for a company to obtain milk from outside suppliers or to obtain it from a company-operated plant? The following are some advantages and disadvantages of operating a company's own facility.

Advantages

1. Lower delivery costs result when a specialized plant operating at high efficiency can use its transportation equipment for mixed loads—dairy products and produce, for example. Further, when fluid milk processing is an internal operation, drivers generally are compensated on an hourly basis, rather than a commission basis, a practice frequently found in the dairy business. Drivers are drivers and not salesmen. When a distribution center delivers milk to its own stores, delivery cost generally ranges from less than 1 cent to 1.5 cents a quart. Based on the experience of several leading food companies, if a full 40-foot trailer, with 700 or 800 cases of milk, makes only seven or eight drops, the cost may be reduced to as low as 0.6 cents a quart.

2. A company maintains complete control over package design and sizes, so that they are compatible with the over-all operation.

3. A company maintains control of special promotions and of the timing of sales campaigns.

4. A company maintains direct control of quality.

Disadvantages

1. Entering the business of processing fluid milk carries with it the problems of finding, hiring, and supervising personnel; providing capital; obtaining supplies; managing the operation; handling complaints; and synchronizing the new operation with the company's existing methods, policies and programs.

2. The entry of a company into fluid milk production may temporarily displace a substantial amount of milk business. As one executive puts it, "Let us say, for instance, that your company is doing 15 percent of the milk business in an area. You are going to take this away from Dairy X when you start your own plant. In the scramble

to find a home for the milk the dairy formerly sold you, in the beginning there are going to be some very competitive days in your milk market."

3. In those parts of the country where contracts are made by dairy plants for the purchase of all the milk produced by its suppliers, a company may be faced with surpluses at some times of the year. The dairy farmer must be assured that his milk will be purchased in the flush season as well as in the short season, if he is to be a dependable, satisfied supplier. Surplus milk must be either converted to other dairy products or resold in bulk to other dairy plants, "even if we have to take a beating," as one executive in charge of an extensive dairy operation puts it.

4. If a company operates stores that are geographically scattered, its central milk packaging operation can be justified only if enough stores are within a delivery range that makes frequent deliveries practical. The company's more distant stores would have to be served by other suppliers, despite the fact that its own plant may be capable of producing the total quantity of milk required by all its stores.

Additional factors

In setting up a new fluid milk plant, many new efficient methods of handling the product are now available; for example, (a) high-temperature, short-time pasteurization, also known as continuous pasteurization; (b) air-activated valves controlled by either push buttons or a computer to control the flow of product; (c) a cleaning-in-place system that reduces labor cost because equipment need not be dismantled for cleaning, and (d) automatic casers, stackers, and palletizers.

A minimum volume of about 4,000 gallons (or equivalent) a day is needed for profitable operation.[3] A plant capable of that volume would cost about $215,000 for the building and equipment, exclusive of land.

A larger plant, capable of handling about 12,500 gallons daily, would cost about $425,000 for the building and equipment, exclusive of land.

Although fluid milk is generally delivered daily to stores, many companies have found that delivery three times weekly is possible, a practice resulting in a drastic reduction of per-quart delivery cost as well as in savings in store man power for the receiving operation.

Handling baked goods

Although baked goods are selling at a rate of more than 7.5 billion dollars a year, only about one half of this volume is moving through

[3] "The Dairy Plant," by George C. Cope, Grocer's Dairy Co., *NAFC Summary Report*, Management Clinic on Warehousing and Transportation, March 1963.

supermarkets, according to a leading baker of frozen products.

Companies operating through their own central baking plants, however, generally obtain a higher percentage of total available baked goods volume than the supermarket industry as a whole.

A central bakery is feasible if it serves a large number of stores with sufficient volume. Efficient production of bread and sweet goods calls for assembly-line procedures and large volume, as well as the capacity to deliver products economically.

About 42 percent of the supermarkets surveyed by the Super Market Institute, based on 1965 data, said they had complete bakery departments—departments complete in the judgment of the reporting companies, in that they were "more than just commercial baked goods sections." [4]

Central bakeries, ranging in scope from just bread to a wide variety of baked goods, were operated by 16 percent of the SMI's members, and those companies accounted for nearly two-thirds of all the supermarkets with complete bakery departments.

Complete bakery departments are most prevalent in New England, where they are included in 60 percent of the supermarkets; in the West North Central region (54 percent); in the East North Central region (53 percent); and in Canada (52 percent).

Store ordering

A relatively simple utility order form for baked goods has proved to be satisfactory. On this form, a store enters its anticipated baked goods requirements for the corresponding day of the following week. Orders from a group of stores are then recapitulated, and the result is a bake-shop daily total order. Thus, production may be scheduled on a day-by-day basis for the following week.

A duplicate of the store order is used at the store to check the pieces received and to provide the store with a record of how well it disposed of the original order.

One large operation, which has helped to set the pattern for the industry, delivers baked goods to its stores six times a week. Each day the stores determine their needs for the corresponding day of the following week, on the basis of selling experience and adjustments for special features and holidays.

Assembling and shipping

As goods are produced, they are sent to a shipping department and assembled in the same sequence as listed on the store order. In filling

[4] *The Super Market Industry Speaks—1966*, Super Market Institute, Chicago.

store orders, a clerk places selected items in a shipping container, either on a moving conveyor or on a dolly.

Each store's baked goods order is placed in master containers such as corrugated cartons or nesting plastic baskets, stacked on dollies of the same length and width as the container. The containers are lettered with the stores' key numbers and placed aboard the delivery trucks, which are usually insulated. Some companies' trucks are heated in the winter and cooled in the summer to keep baked foods in the temperature range of 70°F to 80°. Cooler temperatures may cause firming and accelerate staling, while higher temperatures may tend to cause moisture condensation on the surface of the product, in turn producing wetness and limpness.

To assure oven-freshness, each product is baked as closely as possible to the shipping time. The products are subjected to controlled or predetermined cooling, with prompt finishing, and are seal-wrapped to prevent moisture evaporation and consequent deterioration in flavor and taste.

The entire effort of a central baking operation to produce a quality product can be negated unless the store handles the baked food properly. As baked goods cannot stand rough handling, containers of baked foods should not be thrown or dropped.

Frozen baked goods

Freezing helps to hurdle the staling problem, but not all products in the pastry line can be frozen and still be satisfactory at the time of consumption. However, a plan to provide perhaps as many as 100 varieties of frozen baked products, including whipped-cream cakes, has been announced by a leading baker of frozen products.

Equipment for the freezing of pastries represents a substantial cash outlay. As a general rule, freezing supplements the usual fresh-baked products.

Finished fresh pastries, including cakes, coffee cakes, Danish pastries, pies, doughnuts, and cookies, require the services of skilled bakers and craftsmen; consequently the labor cost per pound is substantially higher than it is for bread and rolls.

Unfinished baked goods may be either frozen or brown-and-serve. The latter items have a shorter holding period than frozen products. Providing frozen or brown-and-serve products to be finished at the store or at home allows for mass production and helps circumvent the staling problem. "Baking-off" at the store, however, requires special trucks for delivery of the unfinished frozen products, as well as a holding area, finishing facilities, and personnel at the store.

Baked products frozen for the consumer to bake-off at home permit consumers to stock home freezers and bake-off in accordance with their families' needs. Consumers also appreciate oven-ready products they may serve with virtually no effort. Although the consumer performs the baking task, she still usually pays the same retail price per ounce or pound of product as she does for the same product fully baked and ready to serve when purchased.

16

REPACK MERCHANDISE

A food distribution center's dry groceries operation is based primarily on the movement of high-tonnage commodities in high volume. A number of items, however, have high unit value but relatively low rates of movement and therefore cannot be shipped to stores in the full-case lots that provide convenient shipping units for the majority of dry groceries items.

Items that cannot be shipped in full-case lots are nevertheless of great importance in the stores' inventory and profit structures. Typical of merchandise in this category are health and beauty aids, toiletries and sundries, spices, candy, cigarettes and tobacco products, soft goods, and stationery supplies.

Because of the relatively high value of this merchandise, special efforts are made to carry minimum inventories in the distribution center as well as in the stores. Consequently, although the movement of these items is relatively low, the inventory turnover is twice as high as it is for items in the main dry groceries area. The combination of high turnover, minimum inventory, and high value of the merchandise places special emphasis on the need to maintain careful control of inventory and highly organized buying procedures. Unless that is done, costly out-of-stock situations are likely to be experienced at the store level.

Repack merchandise selection area

Assembly-line methods of handling obviously cannot be applied to items that must be removed from master cases and shipped in units consisting of smaller innerpacks. To deal with the unique problems presented by this special category of merchandise, special facilities are required. In virtually every food distribution center, those facilities are to be found in an area set apart from the rest of the warehouse. The area is known as the repack room, broken-package room, split-case area, or small-goods room.

In the repack room, master cases must be broken open and the small innerpack items removed and placed on the selection line. The order selector picks the items required to fill a store order and then repacks them in a carton or a hamper. The final repacked order is then sealed and sent to the shipping dock to be loaded on a truck with the balance of the store's order which has been selected in other areas of the distribution center.

Personnel in the repack room are usually selected from the more experienced and reliable workers, since the relative value of a shipping unit is quite high and the chance of error is greater when a large variety of the small items that make up an order must be selected in a limited area.

Conventional bin shelving

Traditionally, the storage equipment found in the repack room is conventional bin shelving. The employee who restocks the bins usually unpacks the master cases and places the loose innerpacks in designated places in the bins. The order selectors then travel up and down the bin aisles to select the merchandise required to fill each store order.

Some of the problems encountered with this method are (a) lack of assured inventory rotation; (b) interference of restockers with selectors; (c) out-of-stock conditions due to the limited storage space available in the bins; and (d) excessive walking by order selectors up and down the bin aisles.

Gravity-fed shelving

In recent years, some food distribution centers have replaced some of their conventional bins in the repack room with gravity shelving, a series of slanted shelves restocked from the rear. Merchandise is stored in depth and when an item is selected, the next item moves forward to fill the vacant spot.

Such an arrangement allows for a maximum number of facings along the selection aisle, and provides a greater variety of items per running foot of aisle. With the selection line shortened, the walking required for an order selector to fill a complete order is reduced. With more time spent selecting merchandise and less time spent walking, man power savings can be achieved.

Other benefits derived from the use of gravity shelving are the automatic rotation of inventory, the elimination of interference between restockers and selectors, easier supervision, and, in some cases, savings in floor space.

The disadvantages of gravity-fed shelving are that odd-shaped items cannot be handled easily, additional time must be budgeted for the restocking of the shelves, and installing the fixtures involves an additional expense.

Order selection

In most repack operations, the order selector uses a small cart or hand truck to carry several shipping containers in which he packs the individual items as he selects them. He usually selects a complete order, following a predetermined route through the selection area keyed to the items listed on his order sheet. The completed order then goes to a checker, who inspects the order and seals the shipping container.

Some repack operations use a conveyor instead of a cart or hand truck to transport the shipping containers through the picking area. This method is effective in high-volume operations where many orders are processed. When a conveyor is used, each order selector works a specific portion of the selection line, and the order passes from one selector to the next, as on an assembly line. This method is called "zone picking."

The main problem in a zone-picking operation is that the selection line must be balanced so that one selector does not have to select more items than another. That requires knowledge of movement rates as well as the cooperation of the selectors, who must be somewhat flexible in their activities to avoid bottlenecks in the selection line.

Basic handling problems

The first and most obvious problem in the handling of repack merchandise is security. Since the master cases are broken open and the small innerpack items are considered shipping units, the relatively expensive, easily concealed innerpacks provide a day-in, day-out source of temptation. For that reason, the repack area is usually located in a separate room or in a caged section of the warehouse to discourage pilferage.

Another obvious problem is the comparatively high cost of handling the items. The selection of smaller innerpacks instead of full cases to fill store orders is expensive. The operation must include the additional steps of opening the master case, repacking the items in a shipping container, and sealing the container. In some instances, the operation also includes the price marking of each individual item in the master case.

Cigarette storage

For example, the cigarette operation may include applying a tax stamp to each pack of cigarettes, thus requiring a special stamping machine that automatically opens each carton, stamps each pack, and recloses the carton. The operation also presents a handling problem, since each case must be cut open, and the cartons removed, fed through the stamping machine, and repacked in the case for storage or shipment. There is often a duplication of storage facilities, because a warehouse may service a multitax-stamp area, and stamped cigarettes intended for one area must be segregated from those intended for another area. Cigarette storage is usually included in the repack area primarily for security reasons.

Measuring handling efficiency

Warehouse efficiency is normally measured in tons per man-hour. Since the shipping units in the repack area are small and lightweight, the tonnage per man-hour is extremely low. Efficiency in the repack area cannot be measured in the same way as it is measured in the rest of the warehouse.

On the average, repack items carry higher-than-normal gross margins. These margins can be converted into higher net profits if they are not absorbed by inefficient handling at the warehouse level. However, potential savings will not be realized if a company operates its repack room according to selection procedures that are basically the same as those used in the rest of the warehouse. Because of the relatively small size and low volume of the repack operation, the savings possible in handling are occasionally overlooked.

NON-FOODS

"Non-foods" may include health and beauty aids, soft goods, hardware, small appliances, books, magazines, records, and housewares. These are nonedible items not traditionally sold through food stores.

Nonedible items that have been traditionally sold through food stores are usually termed "grocery" items. Mops and brushes, soaps and detergents, paper towels, napkins, and tissues are examples of nonedible items which usually fall into the grocery classification.

It is difficult to determine how many non-foods items are handled by food distribution centers, because definitions of "non-foods" vary. Estimates range from 1,500 to 4,000 items for most companies. For companies operating very large non-foods departments or separate general-merchandise stores, estimates range up to 37,500 items.

A 1,500-item non-foods inventory would generally be divided into about 500 health and beauty aid items, 500 housewares items, and 500 promotional and miscellaneous items. About 30,000 square feet of warehouse space would be needed to service some 250 stores with those 1,500 items.[1]

[1] Round-Table Discussion Notes, *NAFC Summary Report*, Management Clinic on Warehousing and Transportation, November 1959.

Few companies maintain separate warehouse facilities for non-foods. Some of the items are usually handled through the repack room; others, which lend themselves to volume stacking, are handled through the dry groceries selection line; still others, primarily promotional items, are handled in a separate selection area, because they are not part of the permanent inventory or because they present difficult problems in physical handling.

Problems in handling non-foods

From a warehousing point of view, many non-foods present costly handling problems. Some companies estimate that it costs twice as much to handle non-foods as it does to handle dry groceries.

The following handling problems do not necessarily apply to every non-foods item, but they do apply generally to the broad category of non-foods lines:

1. Many items with relatively small tonnage are in the non-foods category. Health and beauty aids, for example, are usually shipped to stores in limited quantities. They must be removed from master containers and selected as innerpack units at the warehouse.

2. Lack of repetitive sales of some items makes them incompatible, from a handling point of view, with standard grocery items whose volume varies relatively little from week to week through the year.

3. A high proportion of items is returned to manufacturers for credit, particularly those items that are purchased on a guaranteed-sale basis. In many cases, unsold merchandise must be returned in the original cartons within specified time limits.

4. The transfer of special items from store to store in efforts to clean out odds and ends and "dogs" sometimes involves the warehouse as a central retransfer point, thus creating the need for procedures that are exceptions to the customary assembly-line methods used in moving high tonnage.

5. The storage and identification of seasonal carry-over merchandise create problems not customarily encountered in grocery warehousing. Seasonal goods returned to the warehouse are likely to be in partial shipping units or in used containers. A grocery warehouse is geared to movement, not dead storage, and merchandise that must be held for a relatively long period creates a difficult situation. Unless an inventory control system and a careful merchandise maintenance system are devised and followed, carry-over items may be "lost" and damaged.

6. Many non-foods items are easily crushed. Some come in shapes that make it difficult to pack solidly. These factors cause the incidence of damage to non-foods items to be higher than it is for many grocery

items. In addition, damaged non-foods are likely to carry higher values per unit than damaged grocery items.

7. Because they are crushable and come in unusual shapes and sizes, many non-foods items are hard to stack. This makes it difficult to handle them in standard fashion on pallets moved by laborsaving equipment.

8. The food distribution center employs skilled labor. Therefore, labor rates for the handling of grocery items and non-foods items in a food distribution center are likely to be higher than labor rates for the handling of non-foods items in competitive forms of retail distribution.

9. In many cases, containers in which non-foods are received from suppliers are unmarked or marked in code only, thus creating problems of identification. Occasionally, secondhand containers are used, with conflicting content identification. Several types of merchandise may be packed in the same carton. Case sizes may vary, with nonstandardized quantities shipped in them. Partial shipments or overshipments may necessitate two or three receivings or may result in return shipments to manufacturers. Vendors' shipping units may have to be converted into a company's own packing and shipping units.

Many distribution centers that assumed they could handle a wide range of non-foods through their conventional dry groceries warehouses soon found that they could not easily do so. Many items could not be handled efficiently in the storage areas and in the conventional selection lines used for dry groceries. For example, large hassocks, power lawn mowers, and occasional furniture occupied considerably more space than was available for them in existing warehouses.

Thus, in determining whether the distribution center will handle a wide range of non-foods, it cannot be assumed that the non-foods operation may be merely added to the dry groceries operation and that the only factor is the amount of space required to stock these goods.

Physical handling methods, the extent to which various items may be palletized, the frequency of selection and delivery, and the need to ship relatively small quantities of some items are factors that must be evaluated before deciding whether to stock non-foods products.

Merchandising know-how

In addition to solving physical handling problems, to handle non-foods efficiently a company must also have the answers to the following questions:

1. Which items will sell?
2. In what quantities should items be stocked?
3. How frequently should merchandise be ordered or reordered?

4. How should items be priced, promoted, and displayed?

5. What sources of supply are available to provide a satisfactory flow of products at competitive prices?

A company without the merchandising experience necessary to answer these questions may wish to deal with rack jobbers who supply the non-foods products as well as the merchandising knowledge.

The role of the rack jobber

In return for the privilege of selling merchandise in a retailer's store, the rack jobber usually offers to sell the merchandise to the retailer on consignment or on some other guaranteed basis, thus minimizing the retailer's risk. Merchandise supplied by rack jobbers does not normally pass through a company's distribution center but is delivered directly to the stores.

The rack jobber supplies the necessary inventory, price-marks the items, sets up the displays, and transfers merchandise in accordance with sales velocity in each store. For these services, he receives part of the retail markup.

From the retailer's point of view, the advantages of dealing with rack jobbers are (1) less investment or no investment in inventory is required; (2) the cost of price-marking, display set-up, and markdowns is avoided; and (3) unfamiliar items are handled by professionals.

From the retailer's viewpoint, the disadvantages are (1) control over the space used at the store is lost to a significant degree; (2) there is a loss of control of inventory levels and of the merchandising mix at the store; (3) an outside supplier has free and, in some cases, unsupervised access to the store; (4) because rack jobbers must be compensated for their services, markups on rack-jobbed goods are lower than on comparable merchandise handled directly; and (5) future expansion of a company administered non-foods operation may be hampered. Only after sufficient experience is gained with small-scale warehousing of non-foods can an efficient warehousing system, based on relatively high volume, be devised.

Distribution center executives and company merchandisers must decide whether the advantages of handling non-foods through the distribution center outweigh the disadvantages.

Generally, the pattern is for rack jobbers to be used as long as a line of merchandise is unfamiliar and entails high risk. As a company gains experience with a line of non-foods merchandise, it can better evaluate methods of handling, buying, and selling that line, and can then decide whether to integrate the new line into its own warehouse operation.

Because of the higher cost of handling and merchandising many non-foods items, markups tend to be higher than for traditional grocery items. Distribution executives are continually seeking ways to reduce handling costs for non-foods so that stores may be competitive in price. The handling problems, however, are difficult to solve and provide a continuing challenge.

SUPPORTING ACTIVITIES AT THE DISTRIBUTION CENTER

The diversified activities of a modern food distribution center include many functions that support the prime objective of moving merchandise in and out to serve the company's stores.

Included among these functions are:

1. Salvage of containers and point-of-sale material.
2. Salvage of damaged merchandise.
3. Safety programs.
4. Fire prevention.
5. Sanitation.
6. Maintenance of equipment.
7. Security.
8. Operation of an employee cafeteria.

Salvage of containers and point-of-sale material

Virtually everything made of paper or wood has value. A problem, however, is whether the value recoverable from a material is great enough to justify the cost of transporting it and converting it to salable form.

Salvage practices vary widely from company to company. Where stores are operated in semiautonomous groups or are widely scattered, practices may vary widely even within a company.

Salvageable materials are transported to a distribution center by trucks that are otherwise empty on return trips from stores. Space used for that purpose, of course, cannot be used for backhauls.

Although the cost of loading, moving, and unloading salvageable materials is considered by many companies to be negligible, some distribution executives who have analyzed the problem point out that store pickups can prove quite costly. However, few companies have tried to allocate expense figures to store pickups in any organized fashion, preferring to treat that activity as a by-product of deliveries of merchandise to stores.

Fluctuations in the market prices of salvaged paper make it economical to bale and sell paper at some periods during the year and to incinerate it at other periods. Before determining the basic program it will follow, a company usually considers the annual net income it might obtain from baling paper. Although prices may fluctuate widely in the course of a year, a company may nevertheless commit itself to a baling program on a year-round basis despite the probability that it will operate at a loss during part of the year.

Hard baled paper may bring $25 a ton at a time when soft baled paper may bring $10 a ton and used tabulating cards may bring $50 a ton. These figures are cited merely to indicate the general magnitude of used-paper prices, not what those prices may be at any specific time.

Waxed papers and papers used for fish-wrapping are usually disposed of by incineration or ordinary trash disposal. Whether incinerators are operated by individual stores or at a central plant depends on a variety of factors:

1. Local regulations governing the use of incinerators.
2. Individual store volume.
3. Company policy.

Proponents of incineration point out that when materials are burned at store level, the problems of storing salvageable paper and cardboard (creating sources of unsanitary conditions), loading, transporting, unloading, baling, and selling are eliminated. They claim that the hidden costs of these operations may be greater than the income to be derived from the sale of salvageable materials over the course of a year. Analysis is necessary to determine whether to bale or to incinerate all materials, or to bale some materials and to incinerate others.

Salvage of damaged merchandise

A distribution center's salvage room activities consist of opening cases, removing damaged units, inserting packing in the spaces left by the removed units, resealing the cases, and indicating on each case the total number of undamaged units it contains. In some instances, items that have been soiled by broken units within a case may require washing.

The objective of the operation is to recover as much of the value as possible of the contents of each case that has been dropped, crushed, or otherwise partly damaged.

When a case of merchandise is damaged at the warehouse, the undamaged portion of its contents is usually shipped to a store. Where the store order calls for a full case, the order selector notes on his selection document that the shipment will be short by the number of items missing from the case. The result is that, on some shipments, a store may receive some items fewer than its original order called for. The store is billed, of course, only for the actual merchandise received.

Damaged merchandise whose appearance is marred but whose edible qualities are not affected may be sent periodically to one or more stores for disposal at reduced prices. Some companies sell damaged goods to salvage brokers; others sell it to cash-and-carry outlets or to warehouse employees at reduced prices. Under certain conditions, some categories of merchandise may be disposed of to other enterprises. For example, bagged flour may be sold to a nearby dog-food manufacturer; damaged sugar may be sold to a refinery for re-refining; damaged bagged salt may be returned to a public warehouse for replacement.

Causes and cost of damage

Losses caused by breakage and damage to grocery products at warehouses, in transit to stores, and in the stores themselves were estimated at more than $35,000,000 at cost, nationally, in 1962. Current losses probably exceed $38,000,000 annually.

About 25 percent of the losses occur at the warehouse, with 2 percent accounted for by damage in transit, and 73 percent of the total loss sustained at store level.

Based on a study of three grocery warehouses, of 66 causes of damage at the warehouse, 12 causes account for 70 percent of the damage.[1] The most common causes of damage, arranged according to the percentage of total cases sustaining damage, are listed in Table 21.

A sampling of 200 of the damaged cases, containing 4,400 retail units, revealed that 33 percent of the retail units were partially damaged and 3 percent were completely damaged. Another sampling of 226 damaged cases, checked after they had been processed through a sal-

[1] U.S. Department of Agriculture *Marketing Research Report No. 652*, May 1964.

Table 21. Common Causes of Merchandise Damage

Causes of Damage	Percentage of Total Damage	Average Number of Cases Damaged per 100,000 Cases Shipped
Dropped in aisle	11.3	16.1
Nails in pallet	11.0	15.8
Damaged by tines on lift truck	10.1	14.4
Damaged during storage	10.1	14.4
Damaged during filling of rack	9.0	12.8
Damaged while being taken from second rack slot	6.0	8.6
Fell off selector truck	3.1	4.5
Fell off pallet during receiving	2.4	3.5
Stack fell over in trailer during loading	2.4	3.4
Set down too hard on selector truck	2.2	3.1
Stack fell over, weak shipping container	1.5	2.1
Damaged during palletizing of poor shipping containers	0.8	1.2

vage room, revealed that the average damaged case lost 25 percent of its wholesale value.

In addition to the direct loss of value, labor costs of 5.4 percent of wholesale value were incurred in the processing of goods damaged in the warehouse. Damage to contents not visible by cursory inspection, not measured by this study, results in further loss, of course.

Prevention of damage

Because of heavy losses, the prevention of damage is the objective of a never-ending campaign by warehouse supervisors. They continually call attention of warehouse personnel to operations that incur high rates of damage. For example, damage to cases dropped in the aisle usually occurs during order selection. In addition, when order selectors take cases from pallets or racks haphazardly and leave the remaining cases without proper support, "honeycombing" may result and cases may fall when nudged from behind. Cases may also be knocked from a pallet when a fork-lift truck fills a slot behind that pallet on a back-to-back selection rack.

Nail damage to bagged items may be reduced by using nails covered with steel strapping, pallets with improved nail-retention ability, glued joints, or cardboard, plywood, or composition board placed on the surface of the pallet. Research is being conducted on the use of epoxy glue to hold pallets together.

Damage may occur when the tines of a fork-lift truck miss the pallet entry and strike the cases. Eye examinations that include testing the depth perception of fork-lift operators may help to solve this problem.

Damage to merchandise in storage may be caused by cases falling while being maneuvered into storage, fork-lift trucks backing into merchandise, merchandise overhang, narrow slots, and leaning stacks. Reduction of damage from these causes may be achieved by allowing proper clearance between pallets in the floor-slot areas, stacking cases in square stacks on the pallet if the cases cannot be interlocked, taping the top tier on the pallet with reusable strapping if the cases have a tendency to slide, allowing clearance space for bagged items, and avoiding placing merchandise in aisles beyond floor markings that indicate the amount of free space that should be available in each lane.

Safety programs

The measurable cost of avoidable accidents to employees in food distribution centers may well be as high as $50 per year per man employed. The unmeasurable cost, however, may far exceed the expense of insurance, compensation payments, and other monetary benefits.

The greatest loss is incurred by the employee and his family when an accident deprives him of the use of an arm or a leg, or when he loses the full income needed to maintain his family's standard of living. The company, too, loses more than can be easily measured; for example, the full service of a trained employee, the time lost when workers must be rescheduled, and the damage to property that frequently accompanies an accident.

A sound, consistently operated safety program is essential in a food distribution center. The elements of such a program include: periodic physical examinations of employees; maintaining accurate records of the causes of accidents and the steps that might have been taken to prevent them; continual counseling of all employees who may be accident-prone; periodic inspections of all facilities by a competent engineer and a physician; reminders on bulletin boards and in other communication media of the seriousness of accidents, emphasizing time lost; and periodic meetings to demonstrate proven methods of avoiding accidents.

Distribution executives have also found that appeals to the professional pride of employees in the maintenance of good individual and group safety records is an effective method of controlling the incidence of accidents.

Fire prevention

Before a food distribution center is constructed, planners consult fire insurance specifications to be sure the plans meet the requirements for low insurance rates and fire-safe construction. Sprinkler systems, alarms, fire curtains, smoke vents, fire walls, and ceiling construction that confines fires to limited zones are some devices used to prevent fires or to limit their spread should they occur.

Prevention, however, is the surest method of fighting fire. The following are important parts of a fire-prevention program:

1. Control of smoking.
2. Periodic inspections.
3. Elimination of hazards such as defective wiring, accumulations of rubbish, and use of equipment rooms for storage purposes.
4. Fire drills.
5. Organizing of fire brigades.
6. Systematic maintenance of electrical equipment.

The physical damage to the structure, equipment, and merchandise caused by fire can, in effect, put a company out of business. The inability of a distribution center to supply a steady stream of merchandise to the stores can result in the loss of sales at stores and in high costs of obtaining merchandise for direct shipment to individual stores.

Sanitation

Any building in which food is handled requires a positive, continuing program of sanitation. Food distribution centers have a special responsibility for maintaining high standards of cleanliness as the food is distributed to a large number of stores.

Maintenance of sanitary conditions calls for these standards:

1. Daily disposal of damaged or unsalable produce.
2. Careful rotation of stock to prevent deterioration of containers and of foods that may have been attacked by vermin.
3. Segregation of returned goods that may have been damaged, thus attracting pests, and special attention to salvage rooms where food from damaged containers is exposed.
4. Storage of items such as bagged flour on skids at least 6 to 8 inches off the floor and 12 to 18 inches away from walls to keep them away from rodents.
5. A consistent program of insect, rodent, and bird control, including the use of pesticides, the sealing off of openings, and the inspection of bagged materials under ultraviolet lamps.
6. Protection of foods from water damage caused by pipe condensation dripping, leaking roofs, and open windows. Moisture attracts pests and causes containers and the food in them to deteriorate.
7. Protection of perishables in areas with high air pollution through use of a filtering system.
8. The use of floor scrubbers as well as sweepers. Cleaning floor and unloading areas daily in produce warehouses and scrubbing them weekly.

9. The installation of floor drains in every room where meat processing takes place.

10. Careful employee education in a program of maintaining a high level of sanitation in the food distribution center.

11. Knowledge of the major sanitation hazards checked by the Food and Drug Administration.[2]

Food warehouses may be inspected by municipal, state, and Federal authorities.

Maintenance of equipment

The benefits of using mechanical equipment in moving merchandise are lost if the equipment does not function. Consequently, proper maintenance of equipment is an essential function in the food distribution center.

If a towline fails, for example, a loss of about 9 percent in selection efficiency is sustained, one company estimates. If fork-lift trucks drip grease or oil, hazardous conditions are created in the warehouse. If refrigeration equipment breaks down, losses may be great. Equipment and racks that are not properly maintained may also become hazards leading to accidents.

Thus, an important function of the distribution center is that of keeping equipment in efficient working condition. Programs of preventive maintenance, including regular inspection, replacement of worn parts, and anticipation of troublesome conditions are important precautions.

Security

Pilferage is a serious crime. Where pilferage is a problem, it can severely weaken morale, because suspicion may fall on innocent persons until a thorough investigation determines who the real guilty party may be.

Constant surveillance and ample precautions are necessary for the protection of merchandise as well as for the morale of all the honest employees and visitors in a food distribution center.

Little large-scale stealing is encountered in food warehouses. Where it does occur, however, it may be made possible by collusion between warehouse receivers and outside persons who control deliveries. Merchandise may be accepted for delivery and presumably brought into the warehouse but in reality never taken off the delivery truck. Inventory shortages may be detected at a later date, and careful investigation would be needed to determine the reason for the shortages. In

[2] "Would Food and Drug Consider Your Warehouse in Sanitary Compliance?" Available in reprint form from American Sanitation Institute, St. Louis, Mo.

a real sense, merchandise may be stolen without its ever entering the warehouse.

Some precautions taken to control pilferage include the following:

1. Maintenance of good inventory controls and records.
2. Segregation of small, high-unit-value items in an enclosed area.
3. Maintenance of uniformed watchmen with control over all entrances and exits.
4. A system of employee check-in and check-out at each shift, with examination of all packages and with written passes for items that may be taken out of the building.
5. Inspection of receiving procedures and of outgoing vehicles.
6. Maintenance of good housekeeping so that merchandise is not hidden or overlooked.

Most companies maintain a firm policy of dealing severely with internal pilferage.

Operation of an employee cafeteria

Many food distribution centers are located some distance from acceptable food service facilities, and employees usually welcome a cafeteria on the premises. In addition to being a convenient place to eat, a company cafeteria provides food at low prices, since food is usually sold at prices subsidized by the company. Employees are saved the trouble of changing clothes for their lunch periods and of taking time to travel to other eating places.

Employee cafeterias may be company operated or leased to food service companies. Cafeterias may be self-sustaining or subsidized. Usually, some form of subsidy is provided as a fringe benefit. Most companies operating their own cafeterias try to recover their food and labor costs by charging for meals, but contribute the space and equipment used. Typically, however, a food distribution center will sustain a cost of 35 cents per meal served.

When cafeterias are operated by outside food service organizations, the company does not usually charge for the space used, so that the prices charged for food may be lower than they would be if rent were paid.

When employees eat at the same facility five days a week the year round, they are likely to tire of the food. It is therefore helpful to vary both the menu and the methods of preparing the food. One company accomplishes this by frequently changing the items on the menu, and allowing a number of people to have a hand in preparing various dishes. Several food service employees prepare various items during the course of a week, and the seasoning used varies markedly from item to item. It is the seasoning that provides variety, the company found, rather than the basic ingredients themselves.

Some cafeterias are so designed that they can easily be converted into meeting rooms for store and warehouse personnel; the meeting rooms are also made available to neighborhood civic groups at appropriate times.

19 THE ROLE OF TOP MANAGEMENT

Top management recognizes that its ability to obtain a satisfactory net profit depends in large part on the proper coordination of distribution functions with merchandising, store operations, and store planning.

Increasing awareness of the close relationship of distribution with all other retail food company activities is leading more and more companies to accept many of the major distribution functions as the direct responsibilities of top-level executives.

Although the details of administration are delegated to technically trained personnel, the general direction of over-all distribution activity is determined by top management. For example, the functions of design, layout and day-by-day operation of distribution centers and the installation of systems of receiving, storage, order selection, and shipping are generally placed in the hands of distribution specialists such as warehouse and transportation managers.

Administration and coordination

Top management, however, takes the responsibility for administering and coordinating the entire operation of the distribution center to make sure that its activities mesh with those of the merchandising and store operations departments. Top management is interested particularly in whether distribution center programs contribute to total company profit, rather than to apparent economies in distribution alone to the possible detriment of other company activities.

Research and planning

Research and planning are closely related functions for which top management is responsible. Research consists of gathering information, evaluating it and, whenever possible, forming conclusions, while planning consists of applying the information and conclusions found through research.

The actual work may be performed by a company's research department or by management consultants called in to carry out an investigation and to make recommendations for action. A final plan resulting from those activities, however, must almost always carry top management's approval.

In the field of distribution, top management is interested in obtaining answers to a variety of problems of which the following are typical:

1. In anticipation of future growth, a company wishes to increase its total warehousing capacity. To do so, it may either expand an existing distribution center or construct new facilities at a location far from the existing one. To permit top management to make that decision intelligently, a planner projects the geographical pattern of growth of the stores, analyzes incoming and outgoing transportation problems, investigates possible sites, and, in general, weighs the alternatives carefully. When all the information is assembled and evaluated, conclusions are drawn and top management can decide which course of action to follow.

2. Top management may authorize a study of the economic feasibility of central meat processing for the production of retail cuts. On the basis of that study, top management determines whether to go ahead with plans for such a facility.

3. An analysis may be made of the costs of maintaining large backrooms in the stores compared with the costs of increasing the frequency of deliveries. A decision by top management, based on that analysis, may require significant changes in the layouts of many stores.

Sources of information

Top management is responsible for initiating research programs. In order to do so, it must learn about new developments and possibilities. One way in which it obtains information is to attend and to participate in meetings and clinics held by organizations such as the National Association of Food Chains, the Super Market Institute, and the National Association of Retail Grocers. Management representatives learn from what others are doing about a wide variety of problems and contribute information about their own companies' experiences. These meetings are conducted on a high professional level and are comparable to meetings of engineers and architects.

Management executives also keep abreast of new developments in food distribution by reading business magazines published specifically for the retail food and materials-handling industries.

Research in various aspects of food distribution is conducted by a number of colleges and universities. Management executives cooperate with university researchers by supplying information or by permitting them to conduct investigations and tests in their companies' distribution centers. They also closely follow the published results of such research.

Analysis of costs

Because distribution costs directly affect a company's profit, management analyzes financial reports on distribution center and transportation operations. Top management is interested primarily in what the reports reveal about how well the distribution center is servicing the stores within budgeted cost limits.

Since labor is the largest single operating expense in a distribution center, management is continually concerned with methods of using man power efficiently. Systems and equipment are studied to determine whether labor costs may be reduced in relation to the total volume of merchandise handled. Systems and equipment that may increase service to stores without increasing man power costs are also studied.

Public relations

A distribution center provides an opportunity to show the public how the complex process of providing a steady flow of good food to the consumer is carried out. The public relations programs of many companies start with the schools. Management arranges for tours of the distribution center by school children. The movement of large quantities of merchandise, the operation of materials-handling equipment, and the activity of processing various kinds of food never fail to interest the children. They often write essays about what they have seen. Word spreads throughout the company's trading area that the distribution center has played host to the children, and good feeling is thus generated about the company.

One company has not only organized regular tours for school children but has decorated the distribution center in such a way as to show the children graphically what is being done in each area.[1] Another company places the smaller children in specially constructed carts that tour the warehouse.[2]

Management representatives are often called upon to speak to local organizations. As part of their public relations responsibility, they must be prepared to make interesting and informative presentations about food distribution.

Trade relations

Part of management's responsibility is to arrange plant tours for representatives of manufacturers and suppliers so they can see exactly what happens to goods they ship as they are received, stored, selected, and shipped to stores. If manufacturers and suppliers understand how a distribution center is organized, they are likely to do a better job of shipping, packaging and labeling merchandise intended for that distribution center. And if they are exposed first-hand to what happens in the distribution center, they will understand that requests for their cooperation are based on sound business reasons.

Executives of other retail food companies who visit a distribution center can always count on being received courteously. Exchange of information on techniques and systems of operation is mutually beneficial.

Innovation

Management must innovate if a company is to make genuine progress. By continually seeking new and better ways to move merchandise faster and at lower cost, management may set new trends or sustain temporary setbacks, but it cannot afford to close its mind to the possibilities of change.

New developments do not spring full grown from the mind of an innovator. A so-called new idea may have a background of trial and error, false starts, incomplete trials, and tests under unfavorable conditions. The management executive knows that the only road to improved methods is the rocky one of trial and error, rejection, modification, and perhaps investments in time and equipment that fail to produce immediate dividends.

At one time, the fork-lift truck and the towline were innovations which were later widely accepted. Today, automatic order-picking is an innovation which may or may not gain similar acceptance. But

[1] Alpha Beta—Acme Stores Co., La Habra, Calif.
[2] Publix Supermarkets, North Miami, Fla.

forward-looking distribution executives will experiment with this idea as well as other innovations in the belief that only through so doing can they achieve genuine progress.

20 THE FOOD DISTRIBUTION CENTER OF THE FUTURE

A fully automated food distribution center is mechanically feasible today. However, at present, the cost of such an installation is prohibitive.

While industry leaders agree that increased adoption of automation is inevitable, how far the food distribution center will move in this direction will depend on the total cost of designing, engineering, installing, and operating the facility.

Although mechanization will be used increasingly, a *fully* automated food distribution center will not prove economically feasible for some time to come—assuming it will ever be feasible.

Automation should not be confused with mechanization. Every automated facility is mechanized, but not every mechanized facility is automated. Although the term "automation" has been used rather loosely to describe many mechanized procedures, the basic meaning of the word applies to self-regulating methods of performing functions without human intervention.

A truly automated food distribution center would be designed as one huge machine that would receive merchandise, separate it into store orders, and load delivery trucks automatically. Engineers and mechanics would spend their time maintaining the equipment that does the actual work.

The food distribution center of the future will undoubtedly develop through evolutionary rather than revolutionary changes. The increasing influence of mechanization can be observed in many existing installations. The following are examples of mechanized operations in use today.

1. Frozen foods handled through semiautomated methods.
2. Tractors electronically controlled without drivers.
3. Computers producing orders for replacing merchandise withdrawn from the warehouse.
4. Automatic communication between stores and food distribution centers and between distribution centers and suppliers.
5. Palletizing for both inbound and outbound freight.
6. Movement of merchandise on cushions of air.

These and other developments supply ample evidence that mechanization is being adopted to a high degree in food distribution centers.

Future role of man power

Despite the fact that mechanization will increase substantially, man power will continue to be an important part of the total operation of the food distribution center. However, the food distribution center of the future will probably make more efficient use of man power than is possible today. For example, a computer, furnished with standard times for the performance of various functions, could calculate the number of man-hours required for each task each day. Assignments would then be made well in advance. The right number of men would be scheduled to do each job at the time they would be needed.

Measures of productivity such as pieces per man-hour will continue to be used, but they will be applied more precisely so that the efficiency of similar operations in various distribution centers can be compared accurately.

In a distribution center today, the major expenditure of man-hours is in the selection of store orders. Relatively few man-hours are spent in receiving and stowing merchandise so that it is in position to be selected.

A semiautomated distribution center, however, would reverse that relationship. Picking and hauling merchandise to the loading dock would be automated, but receiving and placing merchandise so that it is in position to be picked automatically would require relatively more man-hours. This problem will have to be solved before automation gains widespread acceptance in food distribution centers.

Effects of automatic order selection

If automatic selection of store orders on a widespread scale should become a reality, the development would probably force a move away from the one-floor warehouse—the ideal type of building for current operations—to taller buildings more adaptable to automated operation. The buildings will not necessarily be multifloor structures; they may turn out to contain a honeycombed series of compartments 50 or 60 feet high, from which merchandise could be selected automatically. Storage machines and stacker cranes, now available, can pick merchandise from pigeonholes in vertical storage areas 60 feet high and 400 feet long.

Today's emphasis on the fork-lift truck, the electric pallet truck, and the four-wheeler as the major items of equipment used in stocking and selecting merchandise could possibly shift to the overhead crane and the conveyor as the major items of equipment in a highly mechanized or nearly automated operation.

The food distribution center of the future will undoubtedly use many kinds of equipment that have not yet been tested or even invented.

Changes in loading and unloading techniques

In the near future, trailers could very well be loaded without actually being placed at the loading dock until the last moment. An invention that has already been patented permits merchandise to be placed on a surface made up of rollers, on the loading dock, so that the entire load may be automatically rolled into a trailer in a few moments. Thus, waiting time for drivers and equipment would be reduced sharply, and loads would be assembled at the convenience of the shipping department. At the store, an entire load would be rolled as a unit onto a receiving dock. Experiments are still being conducted to determine how stable the loads will be when this system is used.

Additional possibilities for the future

The operation of the food distribution center will be affected by whatever changes take place in buying, shipping, materials handling, merchandising, packaging, store ordering, and retail operations.

Some possibilities for the future are:

1. Automatic buying of a higher percentage of items than is now possible, freeing buyers to concentrate on items that require specialized knowledge and detailed investigation.

2. Detailed analysis of items to determine which should be shipped to the distribution center and which should be shipped directly to all

or some of the stores. Such analysis would take into account the individual sales pattern of each store.

3. An increase to 90 percent or more of the items shipped to the distribution center in unitized loads.

4. Improvements in packaging so that individual packages are tailored to fit both store gondolas and packing cases. The packing cases would fit on standard pallets without voids in the cube.

5. General acceptance of the idea of the computerized supermarket, with automatic ordering from the stores a reality. As the cost of computers is reduced, it may become economically feasible for each supermarket to have its own computer on the premises, or to have direct access to a home-office computer by means of telephone lines. With each item of merchandise marked in a code that can be read by an optical scanner at the checkstand, the computer would know at the time of sale exactly what was sold, and the customer would receive a printed itemized receipt. Payment would be made either by credit card or by cash tendered to a change-making machine, so that no cashier would be involved in the transaction.

At the warehouse, the large computer would be "told" what was sold by the small computer in the store. The large computer would be programmed to make up a store order based on the inventory-withdrawal data it received.

6. The possibility of delivering consumers' orders directly from a distribution center to their homes in thickly populated metropolitan areas where land for stores becomes too expensive. Some sites are now selling for millions of dollars, thus making it uneconomical to build supermarkets to serve customers in these areas.

7. The possibility of dispensing complete, hot meals to apartment-house dwellers and of billing customers monthly through the use of a meter installed in the home. The customer would dial a meal, which would be delivered on disposable dishes through a pneumatic tube.

8. A radical change in the mix of merchandise sold by supermarkets as progress in food technology produces items that cannot even be envisioned today.

As future developments occur, whatever they may be, the food distribution center will have to evaluate them and make adjustments. Some of those adjustments may result in distribution center designs and systems that will be radical departures from those of today.

Vital role of computers

Many of the possibilities for progress in the food distribution center depend upon increased use of computers. From control of inventories to control of space and work procedures, the computer will play a vital role in operating the food distribution center of the future.

In the future, the computer will be used by the distribution center to solve problems such as the following:

1. What are the best locations for merchandise at the distribution center?
2. How many receiving doors are needed?
3. What are the optimum hours of operation of the distribution center?
4. How should personnel be scheduled to handle the operations for each shift, and how many shifts are required on a given day?
5. What are the most economical and effective delivery routes to follow?
6. How may alternative equipment and systems be evaluated?

To find an answer to a problem, the computer would be given as much information as possible about that problem. For example, to determine the most economical and effective delivery routes to follow, data on the following measurable factors would be fed into the computer:

1. Mileage.
2. Regular and overtime pay scales.
3. Sizes and weights of loads.
4. Capacity of available equipment.
5. Optimum times for receiving at the stores.
6. Road, traffic, and weather conditions.
7. Relative volume of shipping throughout the day, week, month, or season.
8. Idle time of vehicles.
9. Availability of man power.
10. Available backhauls.
11. Rate of distribution center output.

The computer would then calculate the desired delivery routes. As one or more of the measurable factors change, the new information would be fed into the computer and the answer would be revised in the light of the new data.

The computer can handle large amounts of data rapidly and reach decisions. Because many possibilities must be examined in detail before the best available answer is found, and because those possibilities are expressed in numbers, the computer is used.

Concept of "distribution"

Great strides have already been taken in developing the food distribution center of the future. Perhaps the most important step has been the adoption of the concept that the principal role of the center is *distribution* rather than warehousing and transportation.

Retail food distribution executives view the future in terms of making the *total process* of distributing food more efficient rather than in terms of developing specific pieces of equipment.

Acceptance of that concept has led to the development of the integrated plant designed to receive, handle, ship, and, where necessary, process the merchandise with which it deals.

Further development of that concept would lead to an even broader view of the distribution process. The total process of moving food from farm to table may be thought of as a single, continuous flow. All the subfunctions such as buying, transportation in and out of the distribution center, transportation directly from processor to store, warehousing, packaging, inventory control, receiving at the store, display, point-of-sale recording of data on merchandise movement, personnel requirements, and sales promotion are part of a total process that is somewhat fragmented today. Executives in charge of various subfunctions normally tend to view their areas of responsibility as clearly defined and limited. Development of the concept of distribution as a total process would integrate all the activities that relate to moving food to the ultimate consumer. Eventually a new type of executive position would be created so that all of a company's distribution activities would be consolidated under a single directing authority. That executive would be concerned with the best ways of moving food quickly and economically and would not be committed to effecting savings in a limited area if such savings would result in excessive costs in other areas. The interrelationships of all distribution functions are illustrated in Exhibit 32.

As distribution executives reshape their concepts of the role that can be played by the food distribution center of the future in relation to the concept of total distribution, they will probably develop new ways of looking at their problems.

The bright promise held out by the research, experimentation, and planning of today can be fulfilled only if high-caliber management is recruited or developed within the food distribution field.

Following World War II, the use of the fork-lift truck in food distribution brought about a major change in the methods of moving food quickly and economically. The application of the computer and of automated equipment will bring about the next significant change in food distribution. How soundly that concept is developed and how wisely it is applied will depend on the skill, knowledge, and imagination of the future food distribution executive.

Exhibit 32. Distribution Management Organizational Structure Consolidation of Functional Relationships

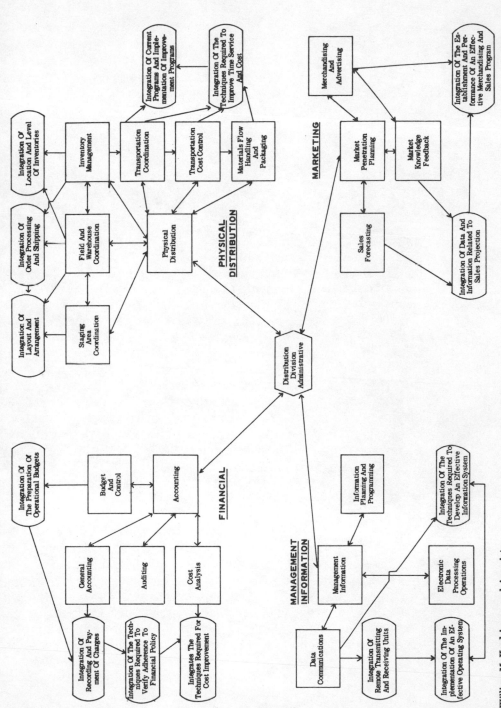

William M. Kordsiemon and Associates

INDEX

A

Access to good roads factor, 19, 20
Activities of food distribution center, 3
Advance large-scale purchases, 29, 30
  formula for storage of, 30
Airlines accessibility, 22, 23
Air pollution factor, 23, 200
Aisle space, 31, 32, 37, 40, 64, 69, 70
Alpha Beta-Acme Stores, *208*
American Meat Institute, study by, 134, 135
American Sanitation Institute, *201*
Angle stacking, 68-70
Anticipated future volume, 10
Assortment merchandising, 98
Automation
  in food distribution center, 211-214
  in warehousing of frozen foods, 166-168
  reordering systems, 110
Average store order, 44, 45

B

Backhaul, 127-129
Backup stocks, 46
Baked goods, 7, 178-181
  assembling, 179
  central bakeries, 179
  frozen goods, 180
  shipping, 180
  store ordering, 179
  utility order form, 179
Banana ripening, 153, 154
Block cuts of meat, 134
  defined, 145
Boxed cuts of meat, 142
  defined, 145
Bulkheads in refrigerated trailers, 122, 123
"Burgoyne Index," *133, 147*
Buying function, 7

Note: Italicized page numbers refer to footnotes.

C

Cafeteria for employees, 202, 203
Central bakeries, 179
Central cheese packaging, 176, 177
Central meat processing, 139-145
  equipment for, 141, 142
  ground beef production, 139
  meat cutters, 140
  primal cuts, 139-141
  retail cuts, 136, 140-144
"C.I.E.S. Reports," *92, 99*
"Chain Store Age," *147*
Clamp lift
  method, 80, 83-85
  trucks, 50, 58, 73, 84
Cleanliness
  of equipment, 51
  of plant, 200, 201
Code book, 66, 85
Code number, 85, 86, 94, 160
Cold boxes, 123, 127
Column spacings, 46
Combination loads, 111-114, 163
Commodity group report, 97
Community acceptance of distribution center, 24
Community resources, 23, 24
Compartmentation, 127
Computer, 88-103, 214, 215
  forecasting systems, 99
  input, 90-93
  miscellaneous uses, 102, 103
  output, 94-96
  processing of data, 93, 94
Consolidated shipments, 2
Construction costs, 11-14
Containers used in shipments, 126, 127, 152, 162
Conventional bin shelving, 184
Conveyor, 58, 160, 161, 167
  double-deck system, 160
  endless belt, 58
  line, 50
  method of selection, 64, 65

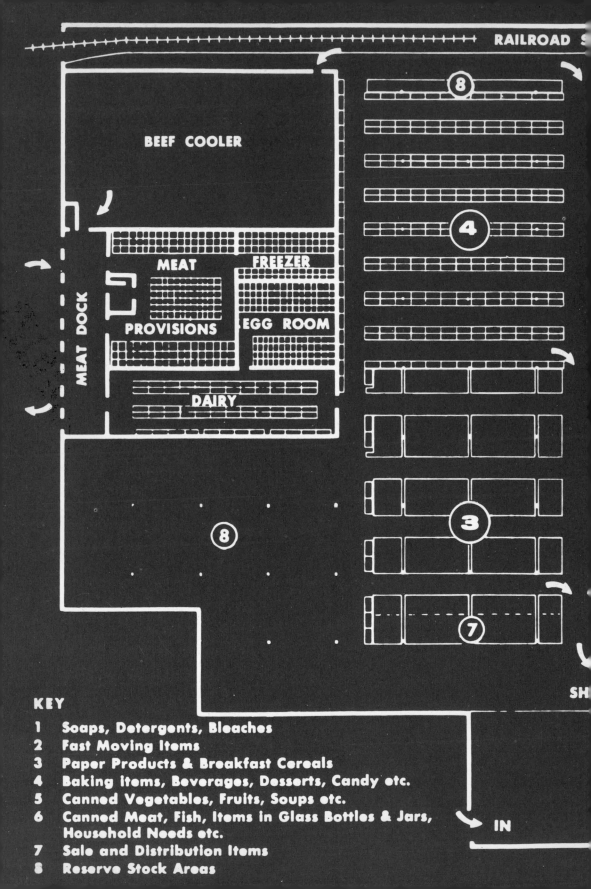

RAILROAD S

BEEF COOLER

⑧

MEAT   FREEZER

PROVISIONS   EGG ROOM

MEAT DOCK

DAIRY

④

③

⑧

⑦

SH

KEY

1 Soaps, Detergents, Bleaches
2 Fast Moving Items
3 Paper Products & Breakfast Cereals
4 Baking items, Beverages, Desserts, Candy etc.
5 Canned Vegetables, Fruits, Soups etc.
6 Canned Meat, Fish, Items in Glass Bottles & Jars,
   Household Needs etc.
7 Sale and Distribution Items
8 Reserve Stock Areas

IN